Galaxies, Nuclei, and Quasars

FRED HOYLE

GALAXIES

NUCLEI

AND QUASARS

HARPER & ROW, PUBLISHERS · *New York*

Contents

Acknowledgments

The six chapters of this book are based on lectures given during 1964 to university audiences. The treatment is intended to emphasize the very fluid state of modern astronomy and cosmology. Remarkable new developments are now being made in these subjects. I have attempted to capture, as best I can, something of the excitement of the current situation. I am indebted to my colleagues for the illustrations to be found in the book, particularly to E. M. Burbidge, W. A. Fowler, J. B. Oke, A. R. Sandage, M. Schmidt, and to the Mount Wilson and Palomar Observatories.

Fred Hoyle
1965

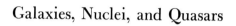

Galaxies, Nuclei, and Quasars

1

Galaxies

The best known galaxy is naturally the one we live in. We know much more about the fine details, about the stars that compose it, about their motions, about its gas and dust content, than we do of other galaxies. However, we do not know very accurately what its gross form looks like, how it would appear if seen from afar off. In total mass and in size it seems to be much like the nearest of the large external galaxies, the nebula in Andromeda, catalogue number M 31, seen in Plate I. Perhaps the best guess is that our Galaxy would look pretty much like this if we could see it from outside.

Galaxies come in many forms. The classification scheme due to Hubble starts with more-or-less spherical amorphous systems, the type E0 shown in Plate II. The brightest, most massive of all galaxies are of this type, they run to probably more than ten times the mass of M 31, or of our Galaxy, and they are perhaps three or four times as luminous. Speaking in order of magnitude, they contain about a million million stars. Two strange features of such systems are worth men-

II. NGC 4486 Globular nebula in *Virgo*. Messier 87; 200-inch photograph. (Mount Wilson and Palomar Observatories.)

tioning here even though I am trespassing on the subject of my next chapter.

There are more faint galaxies than there are highly luminous ones, which is not surprising. What is distinctly odd,

I (*opposite*). NGC 224 Great galaxy in *Andromeda*. Messier 31. Satellite galaxies NGC 205 and 221 also shown; 48-inch Schmidt photograph. (Mount Wilson and Palomar Observatories.)

however, is that the most luminous ones all seem to be more-
or-less identical specimens. It doesn't seem to matter very
much whether you take a sample of a couple of dozen
galaxies or a sample of a thousand, so long as it has a big E0
in it the E0 will be just the same sort of chap. Galaxies
apparently exist up to a certain limit and not beyond that.
Why?

These E0's superficially seem to be very dull systems. They
contain very little gas. Scarcely any new stars are forming in
them, perhaps none. Consequently, they contain no bright
young stars. Yet we now know the E0's are the seat of in-
credibly violent activity. In Plate III you can see evidence of
a jet of something or other bursting out from the center of
the big galaxy shown in Plate II. The centers of all these
systems are most remarkable. With few exceptions they have
very small very bright central cores. How small we cannot
yet say because, in the technical term, the central pip is unresolved. That is to say, the shimmering of the earth's atmosphere prevents the ground-based astronomer from determining angles less than about 1″, and these cores are less than
that. Probably they will turn out to have diameters of about
a hundred light-years, but a definitive answer must await
either an orbiting observatory entirely outside the atmosphere, or a determination with Schwarzschild's balloon telescope. Whatever the final answer turns out to be, it is already
clear that there must be a great concentration of mass at the
centers of these objects, and it is natural to suppose that the
violent activity of which I spoke a moment ago is connected
with this concentration.

The star distribution in an elliptical galaxy is uncannily
smooth. There is nothing like the mixture of bright and dark
regions that we find in spiral galaxies. Hubble's sequence of
elliptical galaxies proceeds in the sense of increasing flattening, the nomenclature being E0, E1, E2, up to E7. Always in

III. NGC 4486. M 87 jet. (Mount Wilson and Palomar Observatories.)

the true elliptical the brightness distribution is smooth. Contours of equal brightness are elliptical—as the name of these galaxies implies—and there is no suggestion of internal structure. As we pass along the series from E0 to E7 we probably pass to less massive, less luminous systems. We have the impression that rotation plays a major role in the later types, although I must emphasize that this has not been confirmed by observation, and I have serious theoretical doubts about the correctness of this supposition.

IV. NGC 4472, an elliptical galaxy of type E-2. (Mount Wilson and Palomar Observatories.)

V. The galaxy NGC 3115. This galaxy has the degree of flattening of an E-7 elliptical, but may be composite, with a disk component. (Mount Wilson and Palomar Observatories.)

VI. The galaxy NGC 4365, an elliptical of type E-2 in the *Virgo Cloud*.

VII. NGC 4594 spiral nebula in *Virgo*, seen edge on. Messier 104; 200-inch photograph. (Mount Wilson and Palomar Observatories.)

Minkowski and Oort measured rotation in the E7 galaxy NGC 3115, but this is not a normal elliptical. It clearly possesses an internal disk structure and seems to be a combination of two components, a comparatively thin but bright disk surrounded by a broader, fainter elliptical distribution. The measured rotation may well belong to the disk component.

The feature I have just mentioned, of galaxies being com-

VIII (*opposite*). NGC 5194 spiral nebulae in *Canes Venatici*. Messier 51. Satellite nebulae in NGC 5195; 200-inch photograph. (Mount Wilson and Palomar Observatories.)

posite, becomes common as soon as we pass from the ellipticals to the spirals. In Plate VII we have the well-known
sombrero-hat galaxy, consisting of a large elliptical-like central bulge surrounded by a flat disk. Hubble's sequence of
spiral galaxies, Sa, Sb, Sc, can indeed be described in terms of
the balance between the nuclear bulge and the spiral disk.
The case shown in Plate VII is an Sa. The Sb galaxies have
less developed nuclei, the Andromeda Nebula (Plate I) is of
this type, as may also be our own Galaxy. The central component is quite weak at the end of the sequence, in the Sc
galaxies. Plate VIII shows the galaxy M 51, a well-known
Sc.

It is not too much to say that the understanding of why
there are these different kinds of galaxy, of how galaxies
originate, constitutes the biggest problem in present-day
astronomy. The properties of the individual stars that make
up the galaxies form the classical study of astrophysics, while
the phenomenon of galaxy formation touches on cosmology.
In fact, the study of galaxies forms a bridge between conventional astronomy and astrophysics on the one hand, and cosmology on the other.

Extraordinarily little is known about the formation of
galaxies. The usual point of view is that the galaxies are
islands of matter left over from the expansion of the universe,
following its origin at very high density. It is easy to show
that the behavior of matter in any particular locality follows
exactly the same equations as does a simple expanding cloud
of gas in the ordinary Newtonian gravitational theory. Given
sufficient initial energy a discrete cloud expands apart indefinitely, whereas with insufficient energy a cloud falls back
on itself after attaining a maximum extension. The usual
point of view is that in most localities the energy was sufficient to give a continuing expansion, but that in exceptional
cases there was a local energy deficit that caused discrete

blobs of gas to fall back on themselves. These are supposed to have formed the galaxies. I find this explanation unsatisfactory because there is nothing to define the scale of a galaxy. Why should there be the curious upper limit to the mass and brightness that I described before? It has been suggested that the temperature of the gas, or of radiation that may be present, might have played an important role in determining these quantities. However, temperature could only serve to define a *lower* limit to the masses of the galaxies, not an *upper* limit. For this reason I doubt whether a solution of the problem can lie in this direction.

A second conventional point of view is that rotation, more precisely angular momentum, is a powerful factor in determining the type of a galaxy. Thus the sequence of elliptical galaxies, E0 to E7, is taken as one of increasing angular momentum, while the angular-momentum factor is taken as even more of a controlling influence in the spirals. I have the following difficulty with this concept. If gravitation and rotation are the main factors determining the type of a galaxy, then in my view all galaxies should have exactly the same structure. They could be different in mass, luminosity, and size, but their shapes would always be the same. The critical factor in deciding shape is quite clearly the moment at which stars form, and this moment can only depend on the ratio of gravitational and rotational forces, if indeed these are the only two factors in the problem. The same ratio also determines shape, so that shape and star formation should always proceed together. That is to say, all galaxies should fragment into stars when, in their contraction, a particular shape is reached, the shape corresponding to some definite ratio of these forces. Plainly, however, this is not the case—galaxies are of widely different shapes. Indeed it is the sizes of galaxies that tend to be always much the same; at any rate size is a more constant quantity among the main class of galaxy than shape, mass, or luminosity. We can safely conclude that other considerations must enter the problem.

Why is the moment of star formation so important? Because once stars are formed little change takes place in their over-all geometrical arrangement. At an early stage of contraction of a gas cloud it is likely that the cloud is more or less spherical in shape. As contraction proceeds, and I am speaking now about *gas*, there is a gradual flattening of the cloud as rotational forces become more important. Ultimately the gas will settle into a thin disk. Should stars not be formed until after the gas has reached such a disk, then evidently we shall have a flat distribution of stars of the kind found in spirals, and in the later ellipticals. But if stars form at an early stage of contraction, when the cloud is pretty well spherical, the star distribution will correspond to what we find in the early members of the elliptical sequence. Hence we see that if a suitable control could be established over the moment of star formation it would be possible to go a long way toward understanding the different kinds of galaxy.

Star formation goes on in our Galaxy in clouds like those shown in Plate IX. The factors we believe to control the process are made up of four different kinds of forces, not just gravitational and rotary forces. Additionally, magnetic forces and pressure forces must be considered, and the operation of these latter forces depends on complicated and rather surprising factors, such as the presence or absence of fine grains of dust in the gas. Indeed, the whole issue could turn on the presence or absence of dust grains. In Plate X we can see that a huge lane of dust is present. This is a special elliptical galaxy, NGC 5128, which I shall be discussing in my next chapter. It comes as a surprise to find dust associated with what seems to be an elliptical galaxy. Dust is a common feature of the spirals. Until recently it was thought to be essentially absent from all ellipticals.

IX. NGC 1976 Great Nebula in *Orion*. Messier 42; 100-inch photograph. (Mount Wilson and Palomar Observatories.)

X. NGC 5128. This object is a strong radio source; 200-inch photograph. (Mount Wilson and Palomar Observatories.)

These considerations present a real puzzle if you think them through. What is the chemical composition of the dust grains? The most likely substances are common ice and graphite. In fact, the grains may well be a composite mixture of both ice and graphite. To obtain ice we require water, which contains oxygen, while graphite consists of carbon. Both these elements are produced in stars, as we shall see in a later chapter. But how did this happen, if we can't have any stars until after we have dust? Which came first the chicken or the egg?

So far I have been considering only the conventional ideas about galaxy formation. Now I would like to say a little about some new results, and also touch on a new speculation.

We can be quite sure that rotation does have importance in the spirals. As a result of the observational work of Burbidge, Burbidge, and Prendergast, it has become possible to determine the mass distribution in the disks of a number of flat Sc spirals. Knowing the mass distributions, and also using the measured rotational velocities, the distribution of angular momentum can easily be worked out. It turns out to be substantially identical with the angular-momentum distribution of a uniformly rotating cloud. This points pretty strongly to the view that the disks of spirals have *condensed* from such clouds, and that star formation was weak or absent until after the gas had condensed to disklike forms.

It should be emphasized that these results apply to Sc galaxies, which you remember are galaxies with only very weak elliptical components. Similar ideas applied to Sb and Sa galaxies encounter the difficulty of explaining the origin of the elliptical component. Consider Plate VII again. It is entirely possible that the disk component was formed by the condensation of a cloud, exactly as for Sc galaxies. But what about the big nuclear bulge? The same question applies to Sb galaxies, although in a lesser degree.

In our own Galaxy we encounter the same problem when we attempt to explain the origin of the galactic halo. This constitutes the system of globular clusters, high velocity stars, and the galactic nucleus. Baade distinguished the two components, disk and halo, as Types I and II respectively. The stars of Type II, constituting a flattened elliptical system with axes in a ratio of about 1:2, contain perhaps one-tenth of the total mass of the Galaxy. How did this halo come into being? The usual idea is that the halo stars were the first to condense; i.e., they formed at a stage before the condensing gas cloud, which finally comprised the Galaxy, had reached a disk structure. Why then, one might ask, did the rest of the cloud not also form into stars, so that the Galaxy became an elliptical of type about E4, instead of a spiral? No convincing answer has been given to this question and it is hard to see what could be suggested. It should be the first stars that are the most difficult to form, if only because of the dust problem. Once the first stars have condensed, further star formation should be easier not harder. Another idea is that two clouds might have gone to form the Galaxy, an initial cloud that managed to fragment into stars at an early stage before reaching a disk, and a later cloud that did not fragment until after it reached a disk. Once again it is hard to see how this could be, since the order of star formation seems to be the wrong way round. Perhaps we could employ the idea of two clouds by making the halo cloud the second one, but this goes against popular opinion, which holds that the halo stars are older than those in the disk.

I have a strong feeling that a valuable clue to the solution of this problem comes from the fact that the angular velocity of rotation of the halo seems to be much less than that of the disk. This is certainly in opposition to the idea that both components come from the same cloud. The surprising thing is that it seems possible that the halo has no rotation at all.

By this I mean that the halo system as a whole has zero net angular momentum, that as many halo stars possess retrograde motion as possess direct rotation. If this can be established it would seem doubtful that the halo *ever came from outside*.

From an analysis of the motions of local stars, Eggen has separated out a group of several hundred high-velocity stars that can be regarded as belonging to the halo system. They possess two remarkable properties. First, they show little or no systematic rotation. Second, although many of them move in orbits that take them far away from the galactic center, they nevertheless dip close into the central regions of the Galaxy, quite a number going indeed essentially to the very center, exactly as if the gas from which they formed was expelled violently from the center. In the next chapter I shall be discussing many cases where gas comes out of the centers of galaxies, so there is confirmation that processes leading to the expulsion of material actually do occur. There can hardly be any quarrel with this statement. Where the controversy comes in is in deciding whether gas must first fall into the middle from outside before it gets expelled. Common sense would tell us that this has to be the case. However, infall has not so far been observed, whereas there is lots of evidence of expulsion, as we shall see later. Moreover, it is difficult to understand how material could have so little angular momentum as to permit it to fall into the very center. I suppose one might seek to exchange angular momentum between infalling gas and gas already present in the disk, perhaps through the agency of a magnetic field. One might attempt to build a theory in which gas falls into the center along the polar axis of a galaxy, and then flows out of the center in the plane of the disk, and this is perhaps the most conservative way of coming to grips with the problem.

It often happens in astronomy that conservative ideas do

not pay very well, especially when dealing with a quite new phenomenon. In the present case there are indications that all is not well with conservatism. For instance, a gentle flow out of the center is not sufficient to explain the origin of the halo. We require a violent expulsion, not just in the plane of the disk, but in all directions. Not merely single stars but whole clusters, the globular clusters, seem as if they were flung out. The violence of the phenomenon probably caused a considerable fraction of the material to escape entirely from the Galaxy. Stars are known with orbits that take them away from the center to distances upward of a hundred thousand light-years, and at least one star cluster is known that is situated nearly a million light-years away, and which has probably escaped entirely from the Galaxy. It is also possible that the faint dwarf galaxies, several of which exist at about a million light-years from the Galaxy, were formed out of debris expelled from the galactic center, or from the center of M 31.

The energy necessary for the expulsion of such material must be generated internally; the turbulent energy resulting from infall hardly seems adequate. The thought presents itself that nuclear energy may have been responsible, but not nuclear energy generated in stars—for at this stage we have no stars. I spoke at an earlier stage of the need for the production of carbon and oxygen *before* star formation. It is an attractive idea that these dust-forming elements may have been synthesized exactly at this stage. But in what kind of body? The scale must be vastly greater than single stars. We are only just beginning to have ideas on what might be involved, and once again this will be a topic for later chapters.

If we take the view that the halo system of our Galaxy was produced in a large-scale violent event, or events, it becomes natural to suppose that a similar process was responsible for the origin of elliptical galaxies, perhaps even for whole groups of galaxies. Particularly, it is attractive to suppose that the great systems of type E0 are produced from inside, not from outside. The less massive flattened ellipticals, say of type E5, could be expelled debris from a major event involving the origin of a more massive E0 system. One is led to

XI. Cluster of nebulae in *Corona Borealis*. 200-inch photograph. (Mount Wilson and Palomar Observatories.)

wonder whether whole clusters, such as we see in Plate XI, might not have developed in this way. If we think in these terms the process becomes of major cosmological importance. It becomes difficult, or impossible, to think in terms of a simple condensation followed by expulsion. Angular-momentum difficulties are obvious, and no simple picture of angular-momentum transfer between a rotating disk and infalling material, such as we might have for our own Galaxy, will suffice. Rather we are confronted by what may be the connecting link between ordinary astronomy and cosmology. Nobody who has studied the implications of cosmology can doubt, I think, that some such link is required.

At an early stage in this chapter I emphasized that a profoundly unsatisfactory feature of present-day cosmologies is their failure to grapple in any quantitative detail with the problem of the origin of galaxies. Here we have the same problem, approached not from the cosmological side, but from that of ordinary astronomy. By this I mean that we are inevitably confronted with the problem by making comparatively local observations, on our own Galaxy and on comparatively nearby galaxies. It is not necessary to look far away into the depths of space to perceive that something very unusual must be involved, and that our concepts of galaxy formation, even our concepts of star formation and nucleosynthesis, may be in for some rude shocks.

What now do we find if we observe galaxies at great distances? In Figure 1 we see the famous relation between the red shift of the spectrum lines and the magnitudes of the brightest galaxies in clusters. This particular figure is due to Allan Sandage. The red shifts are interpreted as symbolic velocities. An object moving away from us under ordinary flat-space conditions shows a similar red shift, and these are the velocities that such an object would have to have in order to give the same shifts as are actually observed. This is simply

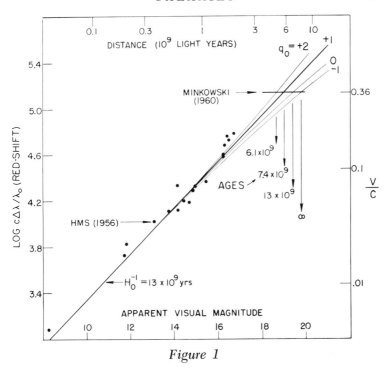

Figure 1

a way of describing the observations; there is no suggestion that we are really dealing with flat space of course. If the brightest galaxies in clusters all come up to what I have already described as the upper limit for galaxies, then the horizontal scale is a measure of distance, and we have a relation between velocity and distance—Hubble's well-known relation $V = Hr$, V the velocity, r the distance, and H a constant known as the Hubble constant. The numerical value of H, as determined from Figure 1, is such that its reciprocal, H^{-1}, is a little above ten billion years. This length of time has the following interpretation.

If this expansion indicated by the red shifts has always been the same as it is now; that is to say, if the red shift from a particular galaxy has always had the same value, then the universe came into being a time H^{-1} ago, about 13 billion years ago. It began as infinitely dense, infinitely hot, gas filling an infinite space. In principle it is possible to decide whether or not this was so by looking at galaxies at great distance. If they turn out to lie on the curve marked zero in Figure 1, then the situation we have just been discussing is the correct picture. If on the other hand, the distant galaxies turn out to lie on a line intermediate between that marked zero and that marked +1, the universe began in a similar high-density, high-temperature state a time $\frac{2}{3} H^{-1}$, about seven or eight billion years ago, and the expansion has been steadily slowing down. Although it will go on slowing down, it will never actually stop.

The observed galaxies shown in Figure 1 would favor the latter case—they would even favor a curve such as that marked +1, to which I will refer in a moment. However, this interpretation is contingent on all the observed galaxies having precisely the same luminosities. A difference by only a factor 2 between nearby and distant galaxies would completely change the situation, from the curve −1 to the curve +1 for instance. Why should the galaxies at great distance have systematically different luminosities from those that are close by? Because we observe the latter as they are now, at the present time, whereas we observe distant galaxies as they were at the moment when the light from them started on its journey towards us. For distant galaxies that would be some three or four billion years ago, and in such a long time it is likely that systematic chances occur that are large enough to spoil the interpretation of these curves. The situation would be better if still more distant galaxies could be observed, because, as you can see, the different curves spread apart from each other as the distance increases. Sandage has made estimates, and concludes that when allowance is made for this luminosity effect the galaxies lie near the zero curve, but the uncertainties are such that anything between -1 and $+1$ remains possible. These two cases have special interest as we will now see.

The curve for $+1$ corresponds to a universe that falls back on itself. That is to say, the universe expands to a state of maximum extension and then starts contracting. What happens at the end of contraction? The simplest mathematical attack on this problem requires the universe to go back to a state of high density and high temperature, and ultimately to vanish in a singularity. It was suggested a few years ago that the effect of a general rotation of the universe might possibly change this conclusion and might cause the universe to "bounce" back, so that instead of starting with a singularity and going back to a singularity there would be an unending series of oscillations. This idea is attractive to many physicists because it is the only cosmology in which the problem of the origin of nucleons can be avoided. If the universe began a finite time ago then all nucleons originated at that time, and a proper system of physics must seek to describe their origin, which is the position that I myself maintain in cosmology.

The idea that rotation could lead to oscillation did not work out. The more complicated mathematics of this case have yielded to treatment, and show that rotation does not prevent the universe from collapsing into a singularity. The next step has been to complicate matters still further, the argument being that, if no simplifications at all are permitted in the mathematical equations, it may turn out that a bounce takes place. This in particular is the view of Russian cosmologists.

It is very difficult to know how to deal with an opponent who when he loses an argument insists that if only things were made more complicated he would win it. I suppose that in the next few years we shall just have to plough through the agony of dealing with the more complicated situation, although I have little doubt that the whole thing will prove just as hopeless as it was before. My reason for this belief is that, in all dynamically-oscillating systems that I know of, a static-equilibrium state or a steady state exists somewhere between the extremes of the oscillation. It is true that experience in this respect is confined to finite, localized systems. But in an oscillating cosmology the whole universe must be finite both in total mass and in volume. Moreover, in those cases so far treated, the mathematical structure of the equations is similar to those we know for local systems. The point I am making is that no static solution or steady-state solution of the required type has been found. The only known static solution for the universe is the one found by Einstein, and Einstein's solution is not appropriate in this problem. The discovery of such a solution should be a far simpler matter than the solution of the complete dynamic calculation, so I regard the continued failure to find either a static solution or a steady-state one as a strong indication that oscillations are not possible.

As I say, the alternative to an oscillating universe is to admit that nucleons must originate in some way. Over the past decade, together with several colleagues, I have tried to treat the problem of the origin of nucleons in accordance with the usual methods adopted in physics; that is to say working from an action principle, the condition for the origin of a particle being that the action is invariant with respect to the appearance of a particle, or particles. It turns out that such a theory can be constructed, and that it immediately forbids the singularities that plague the more orthodox forms of cosmology. What the further implications of this cosmology are, I shall discuss in Chapter 4. I will only say here that a possible implication is the curve −1 of Figure 1.

I spoke at some length about the formation of galaxies, and

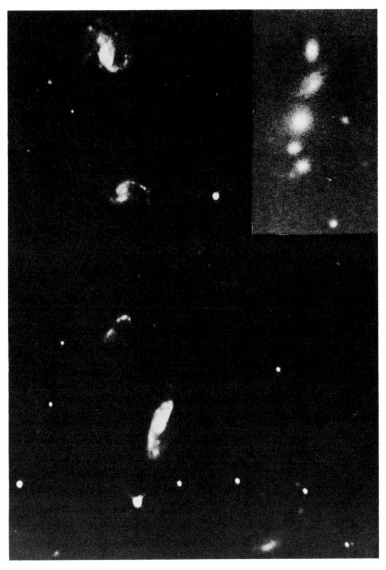

XII and XIII. Examples of chains of galaxies. (Courtesy of E. M. Burbidge, University of California.)

25

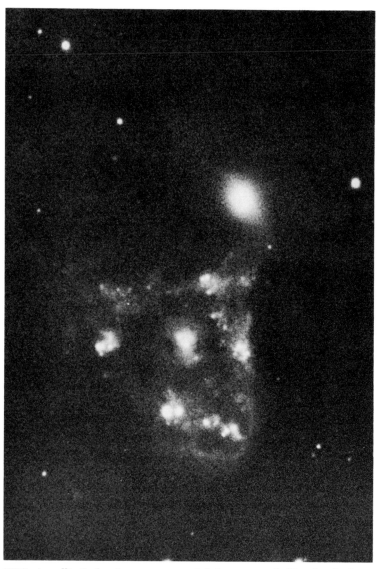

XIV. An elliptical galaxy accompanied by a remarkable cloud of gas and stars. (Courtesy of E. M. Burbidge, University of California.)

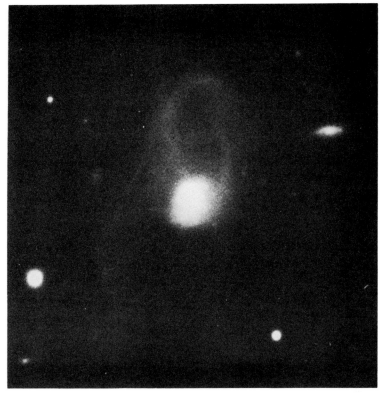

XV. A galaxy with a tubular connection to external space. (Courtesy of E. M. Burbidge, University of California.)

you may have wondered whether a direct observational approach to this problem might be possible. Why not look and see whether galaxies are being formed at the present time. If so, then quite a bit of the problem might be solved by simple inspection. Now that galaxies have been observed with a view to discovering peculiarities, remarkable results have emerged. First, there are geometrical patterns to suggest that particular groups of galaxies might be of recent origin. In each of Plates XII and XIII you see five galaxies strung along a line.

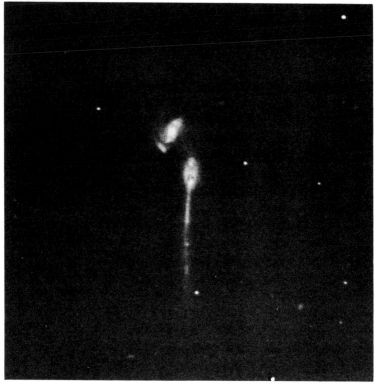

XVI. A spike-like extension from a galaxy to interstellar space. (Courtesy of E. M. Burbidge, University of California.)

It does not seem as if these arrangements can be chance projection effects, i.e., galaxies that are in no way connected with each other happening to fall close together on the two-dimensional projection of the sky. There is both a consistency of size and type in these chains of galaxies. How long could such chains persist? This is the essential question. The answer depends on the motions of the galaxies relative to each other and these would normally be expected to destroy a linear arrangement, such as we see here, in a comparatively short

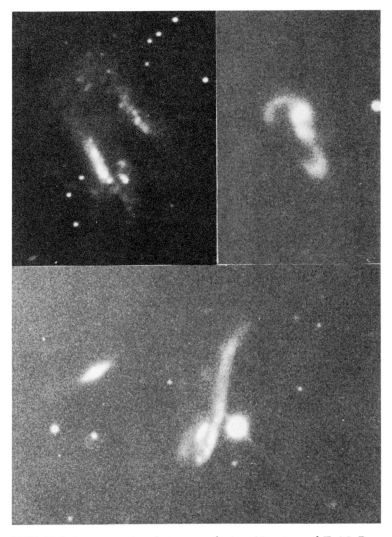

XVII. Tubular connections between galaxies. (Courtesy of E. M. Burbidge, University of California.)

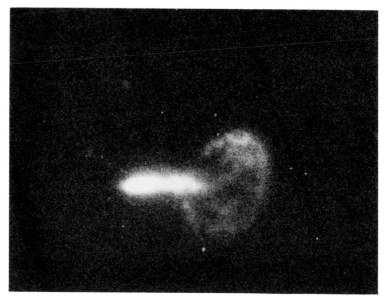

XVIII. Mayall's Object. (Courtesy of E. M. Burbidge, University of California.)

span of time, in less than a billion years perhaps. These chains point toward the constituent galaxies having been formed fairly recently, as cosmic times go.

Next, unusual individual galaxies show very strange properties. Consider Plate XIV. Is this a new galaxy forming, or is it a whole galaxy that has been blown to fragments by some fantastic explosion? Margaret Burbidge, who took the pictures shown in Plates XII to XIX, believes the former, while Sandage believes the latter. The typical group of galaxies seems to comprise a score or so of galaxies dominated by a bright elliptical. Manifestly, such ellipticals must play a critical role in the development of groups of galaxies, and in an event such as that of Plate XIV we may have a clue as what form the influence takes.

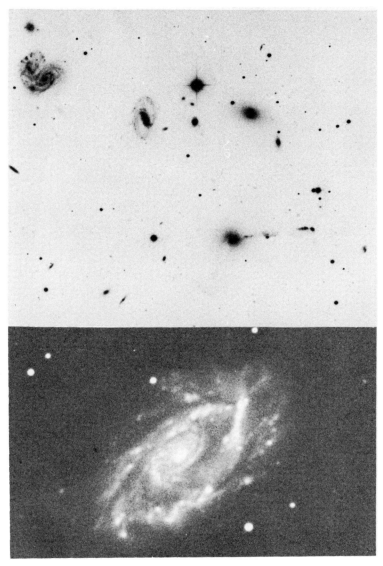

XIX. Galaxies with disturbed shapes. (Courtesy of E. M. Burbidge, University of California.)

Let us move on next to tubular structures in which extensions emerging from galaxies out into intergalactic space can be observed. Examples are shown in Plates XV, XVI, and XVII. What is the origin of the light we receive from these faint extensions? They are possibly stars, but we do not know for sure. Evidently, some kind of interaction is going on between the galaxies and the medium that surrounds them.

There are two points to emphasize about these peculiar phenomena. First, these are not small, insignificant galaxies, they are of major proportions. Second, the phenomena are very likely quite short-lived in many cases, so the fact that we observe such systems is an indication that they cannot be infrequent occurrences.

Finally, let us take a look at several real oddities in Plates XVIII and XIX.

2

Radio Sources

When cosmic radio waves were first detected by Jansky, in the year 1932, there could have been no idea of the remarkable situation that this first discovery was to lead to some thirty years later. Even in the nineteen forties, as the new science of radioastronomy gradually gained strength, everybody thought in terms of a simple process of emission from hot clouds of gas distributed along the plane of our own Galaxy; to be more precise, in terms of the free-free transitions in such a gas. It was true that the emission seemed too strong for this process and that there was much speculation on the reason for the discrepancy between observation and calculation, but I think it is fair to say that nobody then had the slightest inkling of where the trail of discovery would lead in a few short years.

After Jansky, perhaps the greatest discovery of radioastronomy was due to Hey, Parsons and Phillips. They detected a remarkably great radio intensity from a small patch of the sky in the constellation of Cygnus. This was the first radio source. Others were soon to follow. Nowadays, catalogue positions are available for a thousand or more sources; eventually catalogues will probably become comparable with the Henry Draper catalogue for stars, with several hundred thousand members.

Even to this day only about a hundred radio sources have been identified explicitly with optically visible objects. The first identification was made by Bolton, who found that the positions on the sky of one of the newly discovered sources coincided with the Crab Nebula (Plate XX).

At the stage where about a hundred sources had been detected (*not* identified with optical objects) it became clear that the sources are not distributed uniformly on the sky. I think it was Mills who first pointed out that the sources could be divided into two classes, one class highly concentrated toward the galactic plane, the other uniform over the sky. Evidently the first class was associated with the Galaxy. But what did the second class consist of, the isotropic class? There were two possibilities. Isotropy implied either that the sources were very local, on a scale much smaller than the Galaxy, or that they were very distant, on a scale much larger than the Galaxy. Opinion favored the local interpretation and it was at this time that the erroneous description of the sources as "radio stars" was introduced.

The first indications of error came with Bolton's identification of one of the sources with the galaxy M 87, the big E0 that I discussed in the previous chapter (Plate II). Hanbury Brown and Hazard detected radio waves from the Andromeda Nebula (Plate I), so it became clear that at least a proportion of the isotropically distributed sources must be extragalactic in origin. However, there was a difficulty in understanding how they could all be extragalactic. There were too many of them to be explained in terms of weakly-

XX. NGC 1952 "Crab" nebula in *Taurus*. Messier 1. Taken in red light. Remains of supernova of AD 1054; 200-inch photograph. (Mount Wilson and Palomar Observatories.)

emitting galaxies like M 31, although the difficulty was not so severe if they were taken to be all like M 87, which emits considerably more powerfully than M 31 does. Tom Gold argued in favor of the whole isotropic component being extragalactic, preferring to accept the thought that some galaxies must be far more intense emitters than others. But this was not the general opinion fifteen years ago. At that time, the radio "stars" held the stage. I did not quite go as far as Gold, although I did lean toward the extragalactic hypothesis, because, as I pointed out then, there had at least been some half a dozen explicit identifications with galaxies and none with stars.

The breakthrough came with the optical identification of Cygnus A, the first known source. What happened was that Graham Smith at Cambridge obtained the first accurate radio position and sent his result to Walter Baade at the Mt. Wilson and Palomar Observatories. Baade immediately made the now famous identification with what seemed like a pair of colliding galaxies, distant some half billion light-years. The astonishing fact emerged that as much energy was being emitted in the form of radio waves as in the form of visible light. Minkowski found a considerable fraction of the light was in emission lines, such as the 3727 line of OII and the doublet of OIII at 4959 and 5007A. He also found lines of more stripped atoms, for example NeV, showing that the system contained a great deal of hot gas. The heating process was taken at that time to come from the collision of the two apparent galaxies. Further identifications also appeared to support the collision hypothesis, the sources associated with the galaxy NGC 5128 in Centaurus and NGC 1275 in Perseus (Plates X and XXI). Both of these were thought to be collisions of spiral galaxies with ellipticals. In the case of NGC 1275, Minkowski found the gas to be moving at high speeds, up to 3,000 km sec^{-1}, relative to the stellar background be-

XXI. In *Perseus* cluster of galaxies, a radio source; 200-inch photograph. (Mount Wilson and Palomar Observatories.)

longing to the elliptical, and this seemed to give direct support to the idea of a high velocity collision.

What process could cause a galaxy, or a pair of galaxies, to emit such fantastic quantities of radio energy? The idea that plagued scientists in the U. S. and in western Europe for several years was that the energy must come from collision, and that plasma oscillations in a hot gas was the most probable process. Alfvén and Herlofson had the right idea as early as 1950, that the emission came from very-high-energy electrons moving in a magnetic field. They adapted Schwinger's discussion of a similar process that occurs in the laboratory, in the synchrotron machine; hence the name "synchrotron emission," which has become widely used. However, Alfvén and Herlofson applied Schwinger's results to stars, not to galaxies. It was the Russians, Shklovsky and Ginzburg, who first suggested the application of synchrotron emission to galaxies.

In fairness to Hutchinson, now of the University of Southampton in Britain, I think I should add that he suggested the same idea even before 1950, while a student at the Cavendish Laboratory. He developed it at considerable length in a thesis submitted for a fellowship competition at a Cambridge college, my own. Such was the measure of disbelief that it failed to win. I am glad to be able to add that I was not an official referee, although as I recall I did make the comment that the idea looked promising, but this was too lukewarm to sway the decision. Unfortunately, Hutchinson became discouraged and did not publish his work so far as I am aware. Even more unfortunately, scientific history is littered with similar cases, of young people who are discouraged from publishing good ideas which subsequently turn out to be correct. What advice should one give, what precepts can be suggested, to cover such cases? Remember the appalling example of John Couch Adams and the discovery of Neptune! When the news of Galle's discovery of Neptune hit the headlines, as we would say, Adams did not have the smallest fragment of publication, even a nontechnical letter in the press, to offer. History has been very kind to Adams in according him equality with Le Verrier in the Neptune affair. If Britain had not been the dominant political power at that time I do not believe Adams would have been afforded the slightest credit, but this you may feel is unduly cynical. To come back to my question: What should a young man do when he is told that an idea he sets considerable store by is wrong, when he is told this by older, more experienced men, men for whom he may have a high respect? The best advice I suspect is to follow the precept "publish but keep it short." A single page is really sufficient; it would have transformed the Adams affair.

The electrons responsible for the synchrotron emission must have very high energies, in excess of 1 bev. The question arose in the latter fifties of how electrons could acquire such high energies. Also, what was the total energy of all the electrons required to give the observed intensity of emission? The first calculations by Burbidge revealed an astonishing situation. The necessary total energy in some cases was comparable with the energy of collision of two galaxies. So theoreticians were faced by the fantastic problem of explaining how energy of collision could be converted with almost 100 per cent efficiency into electrons of cosmic-ray energies. The best laboratory accelerators only achieve about a 1 per cent efficiency, and how could a more or less chaotic cosmic situation be much more efficient than a precisely controlled laboratory device?

This dilemma has been resolved, at any rate partially, by the realization that we are not dealing with collisions. Geoffrey and Margaret Burbidge have measured the motions of gas clouds in NGC 5128 (Plate X), and find that the speeds of the clouds relative to the stellar background are much too low for there to be any possibility of this being a collision between two galaxies. Now consider what NGC 5128 would look like if, instead of being close by, we saw it at a distance of half a billion light-years, as we do the radio source in Cygnus.

The band of dust would not be seen explicitly, and evidently we would judge that there were two galaxies approaching each other, in collision. This is very likely the explanation of the apparent duplicity of the Cygnus source, shown in Plate XXII.

The death blow of the collision hypothesis has come with the further identifications made in the last two or three years by Matthews and by Schmidt at the California Institute of Technology. Most radio sources turn out to be manifestly associated with single galaxies. Examples are shown in Plates XXIII and XXIV. What does appear to be true is that in

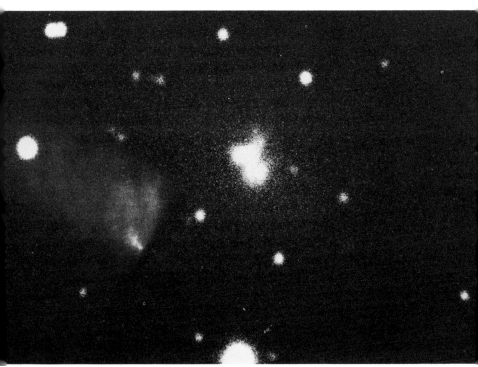

XXII. *Cygnus* "A" radio source; 200-inch photograph. (Mount Wilson and Palomar Observatories.)

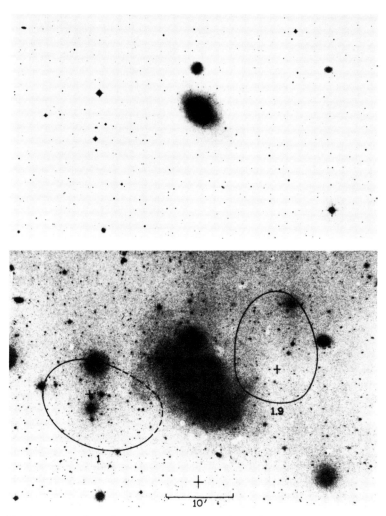

XXIII. The radio galaxy Fornax A. A nearby radio source, shown on a short and on a long exposure. The highly distorted galaxy reaches out into regions of strong radio emission, plotted as irregular contours on the lower photograph. Many radio sources have this double structure, reaching up to a half million light-years in size. (Courtesy of T. Matthews, California Institute of Technology.)

XXIV. A galaxy with two symmetrically placed regions of radio emission, strongly suggesting an origin with the galaxy. Emission of high energy particles in opposite directions seems to have taken place. (Courtesy of T. Matthews, California Institute of Technology.)

many cases the radio source is double, but not the optical galaxy. The spectra turn out to have the properties I described already for the Cygnus source, namely a continuum overlaid by strong emission lines, notably 3727A of OII and the 4959-5007A doublet of OIII. Examples can be seen in Plate XXV, due to Maarten Schmidt. The spectra are indeed so characteristic that the problem could probably be inverted, so that a galaxy with such a spectrum would

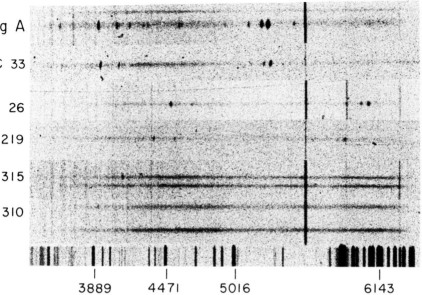

3889	4471	5016	6143

XXV. Spectra of galaxies associated with radio galaxies. The emission lines stand out prominently against the continuum, with the 3727 line of OII, Hβ, and the doublet OIII as the most prominent. The lines occur at different observed wavelengths because of the cosmological red shift. (Courtesy of M. Schmidt, California Institute of Technology.)

turn out to be a radio source. Because acquiring spectra of faint objects is a long tedious job it naturally is not possible to turn the problem round this way, the radio information must come first. To the optical astronomer, radio data serves like a good dog on a hunt. In Plate XXVI we have the source 3C 295 (Source No. 295 of the 3rd Cambridge survey) believed to be at a distance of about 5 billion light-years. This galaxy is coming near to the limit of even the 200-inch telescope. Minkowski found one bright emission line in its spectrum, which he believes to be the 3727A line, displaced, however, by some 46 per cent from its usual position by the

cosmological red shift. This is the most distant measured *galaxy*.

Is there any pattern to the kind of galaxy associated with the strong radio sources? For several years it has been known that the associated galaxies were unusually bright, but recently, through the work of Sandage, it has emerged that they lie at the very upper limit of luminosity, the upper limit I described in the previous chapter. They are the very brightest, most massive, of all the galaxies, of essentially the spherical E0 form. The great bands of dust, which occur in a fair proportion of cases, are distinctly unusual for elliptical galaxies. Presumably the dust is somehow connected with the processes leading to the radio phenomenon.

The seat of the radio phenomenon seems to be at the very centers of galaxies. The phenomenon, whatever it may be, occurs in various degrees of violence. Matter is known to emerge at low speeds from the nuclei of local galaxies, of amount one to a hundred times the mass of the sun per year. Matter is emerging from the center of our own Galaxy, it is emerging from the center of M 31 and from the well-known M 51 (Plate VIII). More violent emission at speeds of about 5,000 km sec^{-1} occurs in the nuclei of a particular class of Sc spirals, named after Seyfert who first classified them. Perhaps the most noteworthy case of emission from the nucleus of what is thought to be a spiral galaxy is M 82, studied in detail recently by Lynds and Sandage. First, in Plate XXVII, you see this galaxy in ordinary light. It is unusual in two ways. It is very dusty and no stars are resolved. Perhaps stars are hidden by the dust, but it is still surprising that none can be resolved in the outer parts. Next, in Plate XXVIII,

---

XXVI (*opposite*). The most distant galaxy, 3C295 in *Bootes*, measured by the 200-inch telescope to date (1960). A source of radio noise. (Mount Wilson and Palomar Observatories.)

XXVII. Ordinary blue plate of M 82. Positive from Mount Wilson and Palomar Observatories.

you see the same galaxy but with a superposition of several blue plates. Now the plumes of gas emerging in the polar directions can be clearly seen. Evidently they have to do with some vast explosion involving at least a million times the sun's mass.

The galaxy M 82 is a weak radio source. It possesses faint looplike extensions in the continuum which Lynds and Sandage have shown to be polarized. This is strong evidence that the light is produced by the same synchrotron process that gives rise to the radio waves. The frequency of the light emitted in the synchrotron process is proportional to the

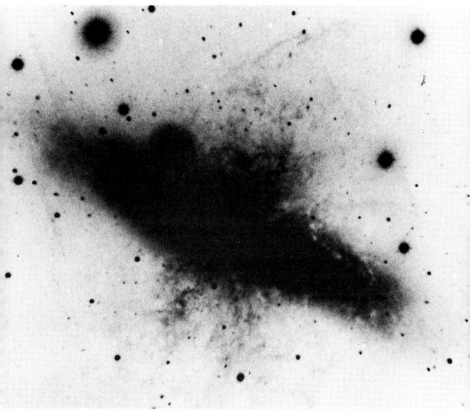

XXVIII. Superposition printing of three blue plates of M 82, showing looped extensions. (Mount Wilson and Palomar Observatories.)

product of the magnetic intensity with the square of the electron energy. Hence, emission of light requires either significantly higher electron energies than in the radio case, or significantly higher fields. Higher electron energies of order 10^3 to 10^4 bev are usually preferred to the very high fields that would otherwise be required.

The most remarkable case of polarized light is that from

the jet which emerges from the center of the galaxy M 87 (Plate III). This is another case of the synchrotron process. It was indeed this case that established the synchrotron theory. Shklovsky suggested that the jet might be polarized and Baade verified that this was so. Following the acceptance of the synchrotron theory, polarization was also looked for at radio wavelengths, but was not found for several years due to an unfortunate circumstance. It has turned out that there is indeed polarization at radio wavelengths, but that the polarization tends to be lost for sources that lie along the plane of the Galaxy. Now the famous Cygnus source, the most intense of all the extragalactic sources, lies smack along the galactic plane. The natural thing to do was to look first at this source, simply because it is so intense. When no polarization was found, the observers became naturally discouraged; if no polarization could be found in the very brightest source there seemed little chance of finding any in fainter sources. It was not until the big precision radiotelescope at Parkes, New South Wales, came into operation that it became readily possible to conduct systematic polarization measures. As I have said, the radio waves *are* polarized, not to anything like the degree shown by optical light, but the polarization is nevertheless there, as predicted by theory.

Bolton, whose name I have mentioned before in connection with the identifications of the Crab Nebula and of M 87, and who built the radiotelescope at the California Institute of Technology, was in charge of the Australian instrument during these measurements. He told me recently that whenever he builds some expensive facility he always likes to justify the money spent, at any rate to himself, in terms of results achieved. He said that he set down the polarization discovery, with all its various consequences, as a half-million dollar write-off, about one-third of the cost of the telescope. He was also in the happy position of having a similar psychological write-off from the work done at Parkes leading to the discovery of the quasi-stellar radio sources, or quasars, which subject will occupy me for the rest of this chapter.

The observational part of the story of the quasars really began with a program at Jodrell Bank, England, for determining the angular sizes of radio sources; that is to say, for determining the size of the patch on the sky that constitutes the radio source. About three hundred sources were examined in the first survey. It was found that the average size was about 30″ of arc. Many of the sources were multiple, often doubles with individual sizes much smaller than this. All the sources lay between about 5″ on the lower side and several minutes of arc on the upper side, with the exception of a group of ten or so, which were as small as 1″, or even less. It appeared therefore that a class of unusually compact sources existed, and naturally everybody was curious about them. At first they were thought to be stellar objects in our own Galaxy, and this view persisted until the end of 1962. One of them, 3C 48, was found by Sandage to have a most curious spectrum, and Sandage and Matthews found the light from 3C 48 to be variable. This seemed to point conclusively to a small local object of a stellar kind.

Meanwhile, two other lines of attack were converging on the problem. Theoretically, it was clear that something more than the explosion of a single star was needed. Shklovsky suggested that a large number of supernovae were at work, but why then did we not observe far more supernovae than we in fact do? Burbidge proposed a correlated explosion of many stars, but what could produce the correlation between one star and another? In the summer of 1962, Fowler and I had the idea of putting all the stars together into one superbody, millions of times the mass of the sun. Two years later this idea seems very obvious, but astronomers had been brought up with the psychological blockage that no starlike body with mass greater than fifty times the sun was supposed to exist. It was necessary to break this blockage. A difficulty soon emerged, however. Our massive objects ought, under certain circumstances, to be brighter than a whole galaxy and this in the beginning seemed very unpalatable, to say the least.

On an apparently very different front, Hazard had the following idea for determining the position of a radio source. Sometimes the moon in its path across the sky crosses a radio source and blots it out. Since one knows more or less exactly where the moon is at any given time, all that had to be done was to note with precision the moments of occultation and reappearance of a source. Working first at Jodrell Bank on the source 3C 212, Hazard obtained a position that was correct to within 2 or 3″, an unprecedented achievement. Then, going to Australia, and working with Mackey and Shimmins, he set about a similar determination for the source 3C 273. Sensing its importance, tremendous precautions were taken to carry out the observation. Mention of these may be of some interest to you. Several tons of metal were sawed off the telescope to permit observation at a lower angle of elevation than the normal operational range. For hours before the occultation all local radio stations broadcast repeated appeals: that no one should switch on a radio transmitter during the critical period of the observation. All roads leading anywhere near the telescope were patrolled to make sure that no cars were in motion in the vicinity. A final, somewhat macabre touch: after the observation Hazard and Bolton carried duplicate records back to Sydney, on separate planes.

The precautions were well worth the trouble—3C 273 is a double source, with two very small components separated by about 20″. The positions of both components were determined to within an accuracy of about 1″. Plate XXIX shows the appropriate region of the sky. One of the components

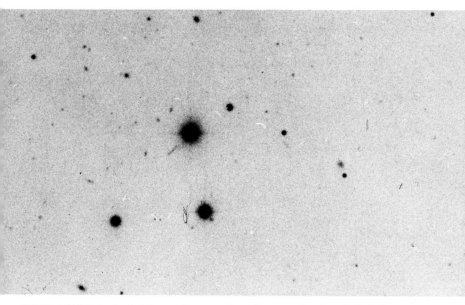

XXIX. 3C273 is the brightest object in this photograph, placed slightly to the left of center. A faint jet projects from the starlike object, in a direction toward bottom left. (Courtesy of M. Schmidt, California Institute of Technology.)

was found to fall on an, at first sight, ordinary thirteenth-magnitude star. On closer examination it was found, however, that pointing away from the star was a faint jet, and that the jet extended to 20″ distance from the star. Sitting at the end of the jet was the second of the two components of the radio source.

Obviously, the next thing to do was to get a spectrum of the apparent star. Plate XXX shows Schmidt's spectrum, on which four lines can be distinguished. What are they? It has turned out that, reading from the right, they are one of the doublet lines of OIII normally situated at 5007A, Hβ, Hγ and Hδ. But all four lines are shifted toward the red by 16 per cent. If this red shift is interpreted as cosmological, the

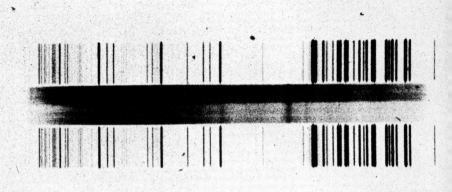

XXX. Spectrum of 3C273. The strongest line is Hβ. The lines Hγ, Hδ can be seen faintly to the left of Hβ. A faint line of OIII lies to the right of Hβ. (Courtesy M. Schmidt, California Institute of Technology.)

apparent thirteenth-magnitude star is no star at all, but an object a hundred times brighter than the brightest galaxies. Evidently, enormous caution was needed before arriving at this fantastic conclusion. First, if the red shift is really a red shift then one can predict where the line Hα should be found. It was indeed found by Beverley Oke, using a spectrum scanner. In Plate XXXI you see the beautiful results obtained by Oke for the various lines. The red shift is undoubtedly genuine.

Next, could the red shift be caused in some other way, particularly could it be a gravitational shift? The fact that the line of OIII was presented in the spectrum suggested that no highly compact star, like a white dwarf or neutron star, could be involved. The density of gas at the surface of such a star would be far too high to permit the appearance of

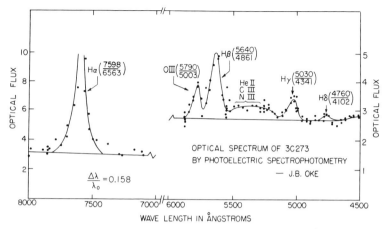

XXXI. 3C273 has a spectrum that is particularly favorable for interpretation in that it shows the lines Hα, Hβ, Hγ, and Hδ of the Balmer series.

a forbidden line. If the shift were gravitational then what is needed is a high potential but a low acceleration. Greenstein and Schmidt have given a fascinating argument along these lines, by which they reached the conclusion that the object would have to be even more remarkable if the shift is gravitational than if it is cosmological. Hence it seemed very probable that we have to deal with objects significantly brighter than whole galaxies.

It was immediately realized that 3C 48, with its strange spectrum, must be a similar kind of object. And as you recall the light from 3C 48 had been found to be variable. It seemed preposterous that the light from something brighter than a whole galaxy could change appreciably in a single year. Smith and Hoffleit had the idea of looking through the Harvard plate files. Because 3C 273 involved a comparatively bright object it had been photographed many times before. In fact, scores of plates going back almost a hundred years were found. Analysis of these revealed variations. Some

inaccuracy is undoubtedly introduced by the lack of uni-
formity in photographic materials manufactured at different
dates, but the errors can hardly be as great as the changes
that were found. It seems certain that the light from 3C273
varies by about 50 per cent in a time of a few years. This can
only mean that the starlike object cannot be larger in its
dimensions than a few light-years. Evidently we have to do
with a compact object pouring out energy on a scale vastly
greater than the sun's energy emission. Clearly this is not an
ordinary star, and it is hard—I suspect impossible—to avoid
the conclusion that we are concerned here with a mass that
exceeds the sun by a factor of a million, perhaps as much as a
hundred million.

By way of concluding this chapter I would like to come
back to questions of energy output and energy availability.
Although we are now enormously better placed to understand the energy required by radio sources, it seems doubtful
whether ordinary nuclear energy, the conversion of hydrogen
to helium, can give a sufficient yield. The minimum total-
energy requirement for the strongest sources is about 10^{60}
ergs. This requirement is a minimum with respect to three
factors, the balance of electron energy and magnetic energy
is taken at its optimum, it assumes no energy in the form of
protons and positive ions, it assumes 100 per cent conversion
from the energy source into electrons with cosmic-ray energy.
An allowance of a power of ten for the first of these three
factors would be entirely reasonable, raising the requirement
to 10^{61} ergs. And if we take the same conversion efficiency as
we would be expected to achieve in a well-designed accelera-
tor in the laboratory, a further multiplication by a hundred
comes from the second factor. The third factor also demands
multiplication by ten if the relation between electrons and
protons is taken as the same as the observed relation in cos-

mic rays. The final total requirement then comes to the fantastic value of 10^{64} ergs. This may be compared with the yield obtained from converting a whole galaxy of material from hydrogen to helium, about 10^{63} ergs. However, it is most unlikely that there is a mass as great as a whole galaxy concentrated in a tiny volume at the centers of galaxies, even at the centers of the big E0's.

It was these considerations which led Fowler and myself to suggest that the source of energy may be gravitational rather than nuclear. Gravitation is capable of supplying about a hundred times more energy per unit mass than is nuclear energy, so that the requirement on the mass would be cut by a factor 10^2, down to about 10^9 $M_\odot$, is compatible with the mass that could be present at the center of an E0 system. The masses that may be present at the centers of spiral galaxies could be perhaps 10^7 $M_\odot$, so that the weaker outbursts from spirals may well be associated with their smaller mass concentrations.*

It should be emphasized that these energy arguments all refer to the energy needed to explain the radio requirements. The energy needed for the optical properties of the quasars is substantially less, and certainly can be explained in terms of the release of nuclear energy. Indeed, it is very likely the case that optical emission is nuclear fired, as we might say, whereas the high-energy electrons are gravitation fired.

What of future developments in this field? In particular, what is the process whereby gravitational energy is converted into particle energy? How are these vast mass concentrations formed? Much speculation is at present going on in relation to these questions. In later chapters I will come to some very recent work. It may be, with luck, that at last we have a clue

---

* $M_\odot$ stands for the mass of the sun, so that 10^9 $M_\odot$ means 10^9 times the mass of the sun.

to the relationship between cosmology and astronomy. The quasars have the look about them that the whole universe, in some cosmologies, is supposed to have had at its beginning. You will recall that in the past decade there have been the so-called "big bang" theories, with the universe beginning all at once, and there has been the steady-state theory, with its creation of nucleons happening gently all the time. Perhaps the truth lies somewhere between. Perhaps the quasars are an indication that the universe has lots of little bangs instead of one big bang, little bangs that are nevertheless far more violent than the gentle processes of the steady-state theory.

3

X Rays, Γ-Rays and Cosmic Rays

Quite new methods are beginning to be used for exploring the universe. Radioastronomy is by no means unique in this respect. Now we realize that cosmic radio waves are in a large measure produced by very energetic electrons, the subject of radioastronomy has become closely connected with the study of cosmic rays. Indeed, cosmic rays are plainly the primary phenomenon. The emission of radio waves is a secondary by-product of the remarkable high-energy events that are going on in space, which it is the aim of cosmic-ray astronomy to disentangle. There are other newcomers to the field, X ray and γ-ray astronomy, and even neutrino astronomy is now being talked about and the first experiments are under way. It will be my aim in this chapter to describe how these new disciplines throw light on the problems of astronomy, and how they aid and complement the more traditional lines of astronomical investigation.

Most of the cosmic rays are protons. There are about ten protons to one helium nucleus, and about ten helium nuclei to one heavier nucleus. Of the heavier nuclei about one in twenty belongs to the iron group—that is to say, to the group of metals centered around iron, with atomic weights ranging from 50 to 60. This is already queer, because in the ordinary material of stars the iron-group nuclei are much less abundant than this. In the sun, instead of one iron nucleus to about four thousand protons, there is only one iron nucleus to about a hundred thousand protons. We know of no material in ordinary astrophysics with the same chemical composition as the cosmic rays, which is a pity because if we did we would obviously have a strong clue as to the places where cosmic rays originate.

Something along these lines has in fact been suggested. In the last chapter I shall be describing how heavy nuclei are synthesized from lighter ones by processes that take place in stars. The iron-group nuclei are believed to be synthesized inside the kind of star that becomes a supernova, so that cosmic rays might owe their origin to the explosive violence of supernovae. There is strong evidence that highly energetic particles are actually produced in supernovae, because all supernovae seem to develop into radio sources. The most thoroughly investigated case is the Crab Nebula (Plate XX).

By a like token the great radio sources, the radio galaxies and quasars, must be far more prolific producers of cosmic rays. One strong radio source is equivalent to more than 10^{10} supernovae. So the problem is to know what fraction of the cosmic rays we observe in the vicinity of the earth comes from nearby supernovae in our own Galaxy. The answer depends on two factors, on how far even the strong sources would go toward establishing the observed intensity *everywhere* throughout space, and whether or not cosmic rays are locally confined within our own Galaxy. Let us begin with the second of these issues.

The heavy nuclei in cosmic rays give immediately interesting information. A heavy nucleus, say a nucleus of iron, traveling at a speed close to that of light, is very fragile. If it passes through a gas, even such a tenuous gas as that which exists along the plane of the Galaxy, after a time it experiences collisions that smash it into fragments. So the presence of heavy nuclei in the cosmic rays immediately tells us that those heavy nuclei cannot have been confined near the plane of the Milky Way for more than a certain length of time, which can be calculated. The maximum length of time turns out to be about a million years. Using this, one can seek a comparatively simple theory along the following lines: Cosmic rays distributed near the plane of the Galaxy have reached a steady-state situation in which new cosmic rays from supernovae balance those which are constantly leaking away into intergalactic space. The mean life of a cosmic-ray particle, before leaking away, is about a million years.

This simple theory has to face three criticisms. Two of these it just manages to survive, the third I suspect to be fatal. The total energy content, in the form of cosmic rays, for the whole disklike region of the Galaxy, is about 10^{54} ergs. This energy has to be resupplied every million years. Now in a million years there are not more than some ten thousand supernovae, so that we require each supernova to deliver about 10^{50} ergs in the form of cosmic rays. This is a rather high value, but it is not impossible. Next, on this picture there must be rather more particles moving in a direction parallel to the plane of the Galaxy than in a direction perpendicular to the plane—there must be some anisotropy in the motions of the particles. No such anisotropy has been detected experimentally, but the experiments are not completely accurate, of course, and the possibility must be entertained that the expected degree of anisotropy may be so small that the experiments would have missed it. Calculation indicates that this may just be the case, although the margin by which the theory can be saved is uncomfortably narrow. The third difficulty is that cosmic rays could not be confined within the Galaxy for anything like as long as a million years if they were not snarled up in a magnetic field. Now the effect of the magnetic field is to link the ordinary interstellar gas and the cosmic rays, in the sense that the gas is subjected to the pressure exerted by the cosmic rays. Indeed, the cosmic-ray pressure is far greater than the ordinary pressure within the gas, so great that the cosmic rays would be capable of actually increasing the thickness of the whole distribution of interstellar gas. The energy of the cosmic rays is comparable with, and may be greater than, the gravitational energy required to expand the disk of interstellar gas from a sheet to its present observed thickness. In such circumstances I would expect the cosmic rays to rip open holes at a number of places, and simply to stream away entirely from the Galaxy, the time involved being only a thousand years or so. Especially would this be the case in the vicinity of the supernovae that produced the cosmic rays.

The more conventional theory, still based on cosmic-ray production by supernovae, is that cosmic rays are confined, not to the same disklike region as the interstellar gas, but to a far bigger, more or less spherical, volume surrounding the whole Galaxy, as if the Galaxy was immersed in a gigantic bubble of cosmic rays. This evades the difficulty with the interstellar gas. It also reduces the anisotropy effect and improves the theory on that score too. Although much more energy is needed to fill a bubble at least a hundred times greater in volume, a longer time interval is available; for by keeping the gas density low within the bubble, the heavy nuclei can be prevented from smashing themselves, perhaps over an interval as long as a hundred million years. This gives the supernovae a hundred times longer to fill the bubble with cosmic rays. However, the position remains awkward. Instead of tearing holes in the disk of the Galaxy, the cosmic rays will tear holes at the surface of the bubble, unless the bubble contains more gas than is usually thought likely. The difficulty here is that several conditions have to be satisfied. Particularly, cooling of the gas must cause it to fall out of the bubble, down on to the inner disk. The gas cannot be stable, it must be resupplied from outside the Galaxy or it must be flung up violently from the plane of the Galaxy.

While a consistent theory can be built along these lines, as Ginzburg and Syrovatsky have shown, the available parameters must be chosen favorably. The theory skirts around difficulties all the way, so the alternative possibility, that cosmic rays are largely of extragalactic origin, certainly deserves attention. We know that about 10^{60} ergs, in the form of *electrons,* are needed to explain the radio emission from strong sources. Electrons are found to carry only about 1 per cent of the total energy of the cosmic rays observed in the vicinity of the earth. *If* the same is true for the cosmic rays generated by the strong sources, the energy associated with each source must be 10^{62} ergs, a hundred times the electron energy. Now within the region of space observed by astronomers there are something like a hundred thousand active sources. These, taken together, give an energy total of 10^{67} ergs. By what factor must this colossal quantity still be multiplied in order to give the total energy of all the cosmic rays that have been generated by all sources taken over the ages of the galaxies? The answer is probably a further factor of ten thousand, lifting the grand total to 10^{71} ergs in all. This last factor is arrived at on the basis that radio sources are probably quite short-lived. Their observed sizes, taken with the very likely correct supposition that high-energy particles are emitted in clouds that move outwards at speeds close to light, suggest lifetimes of only 10^5 to 10^6 years, compared to about 10^{10} years for the ages of the galaxies. The last number needed in this calculation is the volume of space accessible to the astronomer. This is the volume corresponding to a linear scale of nearly ten billion light-years, about 10^{84} cm^3. Dividing the total energy by the volume we arrive at an *energy density* of about 10^{-13} erg per cm^3, which is as close to the observed energy density of cosmic rays, 10^{-12} erg per cm^3, as we may reasonably expect to arrive at in such a rough calculation. The important point emerges that the sources may well be essentially powerful enough to fill the whole of space with cosmic rays, a possibility that would have seemed incredible only a few years ago.

Looked at with hindsight the conclusion is really not so remarkable, of course. The old reason for preferring a local origin for cosmic rays was to keep down the energy requirement. If cosmic rays exist only in galaxies, the energy requirement is about a million times less than if the cosmic rays fill the whole of space. This is because the volume of the bubble around the Galaxy is 10^{69} cm^3, compared to an average volume of 10^{75} cm^3 between the galaxies—the galaxies occupy only a millionth of space, so a factor of a million was "saved" by the local theory. But this was to suppose that all galaxies were about equally effective in their production of cosmic rays. Almost certainly this is just as wrong as was the old idea that all galaxies emit the same radio energies. The strong sources are known now to emit a million times more radio energy than a normal galaxy such as our own, and there is every likelihood that they emit a million times more cosmic rays as well. This was the factor missed in the old argument.

There is no reason why cosmic rays should be precisely the same everywhere. Near the strong sources the energy density must certainly be higher than average. Within a large-scale clustering of galaxies, such as the Virgo Cloud of galaxies, the density could also be higher than average. Because of our own position in relation to the Virgo Cloud, the density in the vicinity of the Galaxy could be appreciably above average. It is entirely possible that the average may fall one or two powers of ten below the observed value. All our argument requires is that the average density in space should lie in the range from 10^{-14} to 10^{-12} erg cm^{-3}.

Is there any observational evidence to favor one or the other of these theories, the local theory or the universal theory? There is hope that evidence may come from X-ray and γ-ray astronomy, but before I explain how this comes about I must go into a rather lengthy discussion on the electronic component of the cosmic rays. Apart from the critically important point that the electrons carry only about 1 per cent of the energy of observed cosmic rays, I have so far said nothing about them. Yet electrons play a crucial role in leading to observable effects, because electrons emit radiation far more readily than protons or heavy nuclei do. Although the electrons may carry only 1 per cent of the energy, their emitting power is very much greater than the more energetic baryon component.

The term baryon refers to a class of particle of which the proton and neutron are the best-known examples. Other baryons have been discovered, sometimes in the events that arise when cosmic rays hit the nuclei of atoms in the atmosphere of the earth, and sometimes in laboratory experiments. The known baryons have been grouped as follows (p, n); Λ; (Σ^-, Σ^0, Σ^+); (Ξ^-, Ξ^0). In ordinary matter we encounter only the proton and the neutron, often glued together, as it were, in the nuclei of atoms. The other baryons, presumably including particles that are still not known, arise only in a world of high energy. The energies that must be abroad in such a world make the gluing of protons and neutrons in ordinary nuclei seem pretty small potatoes. Nuclear energy, the basis of nuclear weapons, is a feeble business compared to the real high-energy world that must exist somewhere in nature. I say *must* because the cosmic rays have originated in some fashion. Although we do not understand very much about the conditions under which they originate, we can at least assert that it must be a high-energy world. The only terrestrial analogue lies in the vast accelerating machines used in contemporary physics. These accelerators carry us across a threshold out and away from the everyday state of affairs to a wholly new situation, which I suspect may lie at the root of cosmology. I find it ironic that doubts are being cast as to whether sums of the order of 100 million dollars can be afforded for the construction of new accelerators, ironic because sums of many *tens of billions* are being afforded to set a man afoot on the ruined slag heap we call the moon. This comparison, between what apparently can be afforded and what can not shows the remarkable degree to which man's cortical activity is still dominated by his lower-brain centers. It is exactly because social decision making is controlled almost entirely by the lower centers, while science and mathematics are controlled by the cortex, that the never-ending moan is raised that science is fast outstripping man's social sense.

There are other sets of particles besides baryons. The group that includes the electron, the *leptons,* consists of the electron, the μ-meson and two kinds of neutrino, written as e^-, μ^-, ν, ν' respectively. Both baryons and leptons have anti-particles e^+, μ^+, $\bar{\nu}$, $\bar{\nu}'$ for leptons, and $(\bar{p}, \bar{n})$; $\bar{\Lambda}$; $(\bar{\Sigma}^+$, $\bar{\Sigma}^0$, $\bar{\Sigma}^-)$; $(\bar{\Xi}^+$, $\bar{\Xi}^0)$ for the baryons. The electron and its anti-particle, the positron, are written as e^-, e^+, instead of $e, \bar{e}$, as in the case of $p, \bar{p}$ for the proton and antiproton. This practice goes back to old-time usages. The notation e^-, e^+ became so well established that it has not been thought worthwhile to change it. Similarly for μ^-, μ^+. It is the general rule that the sign of the electric charge associated with a particle switches when we pass to the antiparticle. But the change from particle to antiparticle involves more than electric charge; the baryons Λ, Σ^0, Ξ^0 have no charge, but they are not the same as their antiparticles.

Our environment, not only the earth, the Galaxy, but very likely the whole visible universe, consists overwhelmingly of matter. There is no suggestion of an equal mixture of particles and antiparticles. As we shall shortly see, this sets a remarkable logical problem. Antiparticles are of course known to exist, because there is a third kind of particle, a third group, equally balanced between matter and antimatter. The best known example is the photon, with its associated electromagnetic field. Photons interact equally with charged particles of matter or of antimatter—it is only the charge property that affects the interaction, not the kind of matter. Energetic photons give rise to electron pairs, to $e^- + e^+$, an equal balance of ordinary electrons and of positrons. This process occurs inside massive stars at an advanced stage of their evolution. It affects the speed of the evolution and this, in turn, affects the processes of nucleosynthesis that take place in these stars. A year or two ago, Fowler and I found that the details of the distribution of the common metals—iron, chromium, nickel, etc., depend in an important way on this production of electron-positron pairs.

The rest of the third group consists of mesons; (π^-, π^0, π^+); (K^+, K_1^0, K_2^0); (K^-, $\bar{K}_1^0$, $\bar{K}_2^0$). The π-mesons constitute the "glue" that holds the protons and neutrons together in nuclei. In a nucleus the π-mesons are "captive," but should some process occur to free them, to allow them to go off by themselves, they quickly decay into μ-mesons and neutrinos, or into gamma rays, viz:

$$\pi^- \rightarrow \mu^- + \bar{\nu}', \; 2.6 \times 10^{-8} \text{ second,}$$
$$\pi^0 \rightarrow \gamma + \gamma, \text{ less than } 10^{-15} \text{ second,}$$
$$\pi^+ \rightarrow \mu^+ + \nu', \; 2.6 \times 10^{-8} \text{ second.}$$

The μ-mesons themselves soon decay into electrons and neutrinos,

$$\mu^- \rightarrow e^- + \nu' + \bar{\nu}, 2.2 \times 10^{-6} \text{ second},$$
$$\mu^+ \rightarrow e^+ + \bar{\nu}' + \nu, 2.2 \times 10^{-6} \text{ second}.$$

There are odd differences between π-mesons and K-mesons. The neutral K-meson, K^0 comes in two types $K_1{}^0$, $K_2{}^0$. And K^-, $\bar{K}^0$ are antiparticles of K^+, K^0. It is possible to regard π^+ as the antiparticle of π^-, but if we do this we must regard π^0 as its own antiparticle. There are not two distinct particles π^0, $\bar{\pi}^0$, as there are distinct K^0 and $\bar{K}^0$ particles. The K-mesons also decay very quickly if they come to exist in a "free" form. The chief modes of decay of K^+ are:

$$K^+ \rightarrow \mu^+ + \nu' \text{ or } \pi^+ + \pi^0, 1.2 \times 10^{-8} \text{ second};$$

the chief mode of $K_1{}^0$ is

$$K_1{}^0 \rightarrow \pi^- + \pi^+, 10^{-10} \text{ second};$$

and the chief modes for $K_2{}^0$ are

$$K_2{}^0 \rightarrow \pi^+ + \mu^- + \bar{\nu}', \ \pi^- + \mu^+ + \nu', \ \pi^+ + e^- + \bar{\nu},$$
$$\pi^- + e^+ + \nu, 6 \times 10^{-8} \text{ second}.$$

Because the π- and μ-mesons themselves decay, the ultimate products of the decay of all kinds of mesons, K, π or μ, are simply electrons, positrons, and neutrinos of various kinds.

Why there should be all these particles, what do the relationships between them consist of, what other particles may be expected to exist and with what properties, are questions for the professional theoretical physicist, not for an astronomer. The development of the concept of new quantum numbers, "isotopic spin" by Kemmer, "strangeness" by Gell-Mann, and the fusing together of new and old quantum numbers in a powerful mathematical structure by Salam and Ward, by Gell-Mann and by Ne'eman, with the prospect of much more

to come, forms a complex and fascinating story, properly to
be related by those who did the work, not by those who read
it! For my purpose three simple concepts are needed:

(1) that "free" mesons, particularly μ-mesons are produced when baryons collide with each other at high
energy;

(2) that in all known processes where electric charge is
concerned—the sum of the electric charges of a set of
interacting particles is equal to the sum of the charges
of their products; and

(3) that in all known processes the creation (or destruction) of a baryon is always accompanied by the creation (or destruction) of an antibaryon.

Point three led Geoffrey Burbidge and me, nearly ten
years ago, to investigate the possibility that the universe
might be equally composed of matter and antimatter. We
ran into the difficulty that we could find no satisfactory
process for unmixing the two kinds of matter. Plainly the
stars are not made equally of the two kinds, otherwise every
star would instantly explode with a violence far greater than
a supernova. This is because the two kinds of matter would
annihilate each other very quickly inside a star, producing
μ- and K-mesons, with an energy release of nearly 10^{21} ergs
gm^{-1}, a hundred times greater than the energy released in
the fusion of hydrogen. Annihilation is such an extremely
powerful process that even the diffuse interstellar gas could
not be an equal mixture. And it has become clear, more recently, that even the gas between the galaxies cannot be an
equal mixture, at any rate if its density is as high as it is
usually thought to be, about 10^{-29} gm cm^{-3}. This is because
among the mesons, resulting from proton–antiproton annihilation, there is a proportion of type π^0, and these decay into
γ-rays. Experiments from satellites would have detected the

resulting γ-rays, and they have not done so. It is true that
γ-rays may have been detected, but not with the necessary
intensity. It seems, then, that not even the very diffuse intergalactic gas can be a homogeneous mixture of particles and
antiparticles.

One might attempt to stick to the idea of equal quantities
of matter and antimatter by keeping the two kinds separate
from each other, by interlacing great blobs of matter with
blobs of antimatter, on the scale of clusters of galaxies for
example. And the difficulty that Burbidge and I ran into, of
explaining how such an unmixing took place, one could
evade by saying that the blobs have always been unmixed.
Besides being artificial, manifestly designed to avoid observational test, there are objections to this path. In the first
place, baryon-antibaryon creation (or destruction), as observed experimentally, takes place *at the same place;* that is
to say, the baryon and antibaryon appear (or disappear) at
the same place. There is no question of the baryon being in
one blob and the antibaryon being in some distant blob.
Hence any creation of pairs should lead to a more-or-less
homogeneous mixture of the two kinds of matter. A less empirical, and therefore more interesting, objection was made
to me by Feynman, at the time Burbidge and I were engaged
on our work. A world that was symmetrical with respect to
matter and antimatter should also be symmetrical with respect to time. There should be no difference between an
anti-observer who reads the universe from future to past,
and our ordinary procedure of reading it from past to future.
This is because particles and antiparticles can be switched by
switching the sense of time. Yet, because electromagnetic
processes do not switch, this cannot be the case. To our anti-
observer there would still be an asymmetry of time—the asymmetry that allows us to break an egg very easily, but which
does not permit even Humpty Dumpty or the king's men to

put it together again. Anti-eggs would still be broken and would refuse to reassemble themselves, and they would do so in the same time sense as do the eggs of our familiar world. There is a strong hint here that the asymmetry of time is connected with the asymmetry of composition of the world, that we have to deal essentially with only one kind of matter.

In this case, if we continue to accept the empirical rule about baryon creation and destruction, we must suppose that the matter we observe in the universe never at any time came into being—otherwise the accompanying antiparticles would also have come into being. Hence we arrive at a universe without beginning, and the only cosmology even superficially consistent with the facts becomes the oscillating model in which the universe alternately expands and contracts. I shall be considering this problem in the next chapter, so I will not pursue the argument here, beyond remarking that severe mathematical difficulties are encountered in trying to understand how a universe in contraction can reverse its motion into one of expansion. So, to end this long diversion, I will come back to the cosmic rays, particularly to the problem of the origin of the electronic component.

At an earlier stage we noticed that heavy nuclei are fragile, so that the presence of heavy nuclei in the cosmic rays shows that the particles have not passed through very much gas, not through more than two or three grams of hydrogen per cm^2 (i.e., in a column of cross-sectional area 1 cm^2, the column being directed along the track of the particle). Now we must notice another fact about cosmic rays, that shows them indeed to have passed through such a quantity of gas. The nuclei of the elements lithium, beryllium and boron (Li Be B) are found, along with carbon, nitrogen and oxygen (C N O) among the lighter elements. The ratio of the number of Li Be B to that of C N O is about 1:3, an enormously high value compared to the ratio found in the sun, or in the earth. The latter is only about 10^{-6}. How are we to explain this remarkably high abundance of Li Be B in cosmic rays? Only on the basis that the heavier nuclei of C N O have been partially smashed up. And this requires the C N O to have passed through two or three grams of hydrogen. So, instead of our saying that the cosmic rays have passed through *not more* than a few grams of hydrogen, we can actually assert that they have passed through this quantity of material. Hence there must have been some collisions between the cosmic rays and the protons that form the nuclei of the hydrogen gas, the ordinary gas within the Galaxy or in external space. In particular, there must have been some collisions between cosmic-ray protons, moving at speeds close to light, and the protons of the more-or-less stationary gas. Perhaps 3 or 4 per cent of the cosmic-ray protons have experienced collisions. Now in such collisions energetic μ-mesons must have been produced. These mesons would decay into electrons and neutrinos, leading to the production of high-energy electrons. This might be the process of origin of the high-energy electrons responsible for the emission of radio waves from the radio sources, a suggestion made some years ago, independently, by Burbidge and by Ginzburg.

A point at first sight in favor of this theory is that the electron energy automatically comes out much lower than the energy of the cosmic-ray protons, partly because only a small fraction of the latter can have been involved in collisions, and partly because only a fraction of the energy of a collision passes to the secondary electron, or electrons—some is retained by the protons and of the rest, about two-thirds, is taken by the neutrinos. The question is rather to decide whether there would be *sufficient* energy for the electrons. My own calculations suggest a deficiency by a factor which might be as small as three but which could be as large as ten. A similar result has been obtained by Ginzburg and Syrovatsky, although the very recent work of Burbidge and Gould arrives at the conclusion that the energy passed to the electrons could be sufficient, i.e., might be as much as 1 per cent of the proton energy.

A more serious difficulty with this idea concerns the ratio of electrons to positrons to be expected from collisions of protons on protons. We start a collision with two protons. If we end with two protons then π^- and π^+ mesons must be produced in equal numbers, because there can be no net generation of electric charge. This would lead to equal numbers of positrons and electrons. The alternative to our ending with two protons is that either, or both, of the protons may switch to one of the other baryons. The possibilities are n, Λ, Σ^-, Σ^0, Σ^+, Ξ^-, or Ξ^0, among known particles. Only in the case of Σ^+ is charge conserved in such a switch. For $p \rightarrow n$, Λ, Σ^0, Ξ^0 a unit of positive charge disappears in the baryon switch. This must be made good by an extra π^+ appearing in the reaction. And for $p \rightarrow \Sigma^-$ or Ξ^- two units of positive charge are involved in the baryon switch, which must be made good by two extra π^+ mesons. It follows, therefore, since π^+ mesons decay ultimately to give positrons, that the number of positrons arising out of collision of cosmic-ray protons with slowly moving hydrogen must be greater than the number of electrons. Yet recent observation by DeShong, Hildebrand, and Meyer show that electrons outnumber positrons by 2:1 or more. Things turn out to be the other way about. The discrepancy is one of principle, showing decisively that the electrons observed by these workers were not derived solely from collisions of cosmic-ray baryons with ambient gas.

The observations were confined to rather low energies, as cosmic-ray energies go, and the possibility cannot be overlooked that the particles observed might have come predominantly from the sun. But this creates another problem almost worse than the one it solves, because high-energy positrons from the sun would be extremely difficult to explain. Quite generally, if we take ordinary matter and accelerate it to high energy—and this does occur on the sun—we obtain ordinary, negatively charged electrons, but no positrons. On the other hand, if the leptons come from proton–proton collisions, positrons must be in excess. Neither process alone gives the right answer. A combination could, of course, be chosen to produce the observed electron–positron ratio. We could appeal to collisions for the positrons and to an acceleration process for the bulk of the electrons. Yet it is strange that two such different methods for obtaining energetic particles should be operative at approximately the same level. The idea has an artificial look about it.

The thought presents itself that if we started from electrically neutral particles, instead of from positively charged protons, we should arrive, pretty well automatically, at the right ratio. Start with some hypothetical, neutral particle or particles, which need not be baryons. Let them change to any mixture of baryons and leptons. Then, because baryons of ordinary matter ultimately become protons of positive charge, there must be an excess of negative charge among the accompanying leptons. Yet some positrons must also arise in a general high-energy situation, for example the decay of Σ^+ to μ^+ and a neutron. I shall attempt to develop this idea in the fifth chapter.

In the remainder of this chapter I want to consider what observable effects we can expect from the electrons and positrons. As I have already pointed out, their radiating power is far greater than that of the protons, even though the protons have a hundred times as much energy. This is because of the far smaller mass of the electron and positron, which causes their accelerations in electromagnetic fields to be much larger than the accelerations of protons. The emission of radio waves is an example. The radio waves are emitted almost wholly by the electron–positron component of the cosmic rays, minor as this may be from an energy point of view. What other radiative processes may we expect? It would be possible to draw up quite a catalogue of possibilities. But rather than draw up some encyclopedic listing I would like to concentrate on the particular processes that seem to me to be of outstanding importance.

Electrons emit radio waves because they are deflected by magnetic fields. The deflection implies acceleration, and an accelerated particle with electric charge always emits radiation. The frequency of the emission is proportional to the square of the electron energy, E^2, and to the strength of the magnetic field, H, and so to the product E^2H. In the radio sources, E is high, but H is low by terrestrial standards. The frequency is therefore rather low; it falls in the radio band, essentially at the bottom of the electromagnetic spectrum. But if either, or both, of E and H were increased, the frequency would be lifted. A sufficient lift could place the radiation into the normal optical range. This in fact is what is happening in the Crab Nebula and in the jet of the galaxy M 87 (Plates XX and III respectively). These objects are emitting visible light by the same process as that which gives rise to radio waves in the normal sources, the process usually described as synchrotron radiation.

It would be an odds-on bet that if we possessed sensitive methods of detection in the infrared, i.e., in the region *between* radio waves and optical light, we should find examples of objects emitting infrared synchrotron radiation. Very likely the Crab Nebula would be one of them. Could higher frequency radiation also be emitted in the same way, ultraviolet light and even X rays? Very high electron energies indeed would be needed, and such electrons would very soon lose their energy. So X-ray emission would soon cease, unless the electrons were steadily replenished from some source or other. This is a point of considerable controversy at the present time, for X-ray emission has indeed been detected from the Crab Nebula, by two teams of workers—by Giacconi, Gursky, Paolini and Rossi at the Massachusetts Institute of Technology, and by Bowyer, Bryan, Chubb, and Friedmann at the Naval Research Laboratory. Other X-ray sources have also been detected but have not yet been identified with optically visible objects. The exciting point is the one I have just made, that if synchrotron emission is responsible for these X rays, as is quite likely the case, the very-high-energy electrons must be rapidly replenished. A currently operative source is needed. This raises the hope that further X-ray observations will help to track down the source, and to reveal the physical processes responsible for generating the electrons. Equipped with such knowledge, we might expect to find ourselves a considerable way farther along the road toward understanding the origin of cosmic rays.

There is a second very interesting way in which electrons and positrons in the cosmic rays might produce critically important observational effects. This second process has recently been examined by Felten and Morrison. As well as being deflected by a magnetic field, high-energy electrons can be appreciably deflected by visible light. Usually we think of this process the other way round, of electrons deflecting light, because in our everyday, low-energy world the effect on the light—its change of direction—is more obvious than the effect on the electron. But this is no longer true for a light quantum of high energy. Appreciable deflection by an electron then gives the electron quite a punch. The same thing is true when the electron has high energy, even though the light quantum itself no longer has high energy. It is sufficient if either the electron or the quantum has high energy. Indeed, it is only the energy of the quantum relative to the electron that really matters—it is irrelevant whether we describe the energy as being resident in the light or in the electron, the effect is the same, namely a hearty kick to the electron. When the quantum begins by having low energy, the kick on the electron is accompanied by a large increase in the energy of the quantum. The increase is proportional to the square of the electron energy, E^2, just as the frequency of synchrotron radiation was proportional to E^2. The analogy between the two processes goes further. If we write down two formulas, one for the rate at which a cosmic-ray electron emits energy as synchrotron radiation, the other for the rate at which it boosts the energy of quanta of visible light—the inverse Compton effect, as this second process is called—the similarity is obvious. In one case we have a formula that contains the product $E^2(H^2/8\pi)$, and in the other we have the product $E^2(\rho)$. Here ρ stands for the energy of the light *per unit volume,* and $H^2/8\pi$ is just the energy of the magnetic field per unit volume. And the numerical factors by which these products must be multiplied to get the actual energy emission differ only by a factor close to two (the synchrotron formula has an extra 2). So what it comes down to is that cosmic-ray electrons and positrons will lose as much energy by the inverse Compton process as they do by synchrotron emission if the energy per unit volume of visible light is twice the magnetic-energy density. What is the situation in this regard in our Galaxy?

The energy of visible light from stars at a point near the position of the sun in the Galaxy was estimated many years ago as being equivalent to a thermodynamic radiation field at about $4°$ Kelvin, i.e., about 2.10^{-12} erg per cm^3. The radiation field in the halo of the Galaxy would be about one order of magnitude less, 2.10^{-13} erg per cm^3, while the radiation density in extragalactic space is a further order of magnitude less, about 10^{-14} erg per cm^3. It is interesting that the energy density of light is not as much lower outside the galaxies as one might expect at first sight. The reason is that the stars of the galaxies have been pouring out radiation for a very long time, about 10^{10} years. The light has not remained trapped inside the galaxies but has been steadily filling the vast seas of space between the galaxies. How about the energy of the magnetic field? It is now believed that H is rather low, even inside the Galaxy, even near the galactic plane. A value of 3.10^{-6} gauss is thought to be a good estimate, giving $H^2/8\pi = 3.10^{-13}$ erg cm^{-3}. So the two forms of energy are rather comparable with each other, especially in the halo, and hence the energy emission due to the inverse Compton effect must be very comparable to that due to synchrotron radiation, at any rate so far as our Galaxy is concerned.

Why are all these forms of energy so comparable with each other—cosmic rays, starlight, the magnetic field—all in the region of 10^{-12} erg cm^{-3}? This question is a poser to the astrophysicist, and no very good answer has been given to it yet. For myself, I have little sympathy with the idea that we are dealing in sheer coincidences.

To come back to the inverse Compton effect: How much do we expect the quanta of visible light to have their energies lifted when they are involved in collisions with high-energy electrons? The answer is by the factor E^2, in which E is the electron energy measured in units of the electron mass (about half-a-million volts, a little less than 10^{-6} erg). Next, to decide on a reasonable choice for E^2 it is useful to keep the parallel with the synchrotron process closely in mind. For a magnetic field with H = 3.10^{-6} gauss, the value of E^2 needed to give a radio emission with frequency 100 Mc/s is about 10^7. Hence, the same electrons as give rise to 100 Mc/s radio radiation in the Galaxy will increase the energies of light quanta, in collision with them, by the very large factor of 10^7. Initially the quanta have energies of about 3 volts. After collision, they have energies of 30 million volts. They become quite hard γ-rays. Remembering our conclusion that the

Galaxy must be radiating energy due to the inverse Compton effect at about the same rate that it emits radio waves, we arrive at the remarkable result that the γ-ray emission by the Galaxy must be as large as its emission of radio waves. Except for the local problem, that γ-rays do not penetrate the earth's atmosphere, and are, therefore, much more difficult to detect than radio waves, the potentialities of γ-ray astronomy may well be just as great as the potentialities of radioastronomy.

Against this one might argue that the strongest radio galaxies are not like our own, that they emit up to a million times the output of normal galaxies. In and around a radio galaxy the magnetic field may well be unusually strong, which would emphasize synchrotron radiation; also the radio emission often comes from large volumes well outside the associated galaxy. The energy density of starlight would be lower in such extensive volumes, and this would tell against the γ-ray emission. The straightforward expectation, therefore, is that γ-ray emission may not attain such spectacular heights as does the radio emission.

What of the facts? A satellite experiment by Kraushaar and Clark, and a balloon experiment by Duthie, Hafner, Kaplon and Fazio, have reported on γ-rays of energy above 50 million volts. Kraushaar has emphasized that his result is preliminary and requires confirmation, so the rest of what I have to say must be taken with caution, particularly as the outcome, if correct, may be very startling. What these results show is not that the γ-ray energy is less than the radio energy but that it is about a hundred times greater! The energies crossing a plane area exposed to the sky are as follows: for radio waves of frequency 30 to 100 Mc/s, about 3.10^{-9} erg per cm^2 per sec; for γ-rays with energies of 50 to 200 mev, about 10^{-7} erg per cm^2 per sec according to Kraushaar and Clark, and about 10^{-6} erg per cm^2 per sec according to Duthie, Hafner, Kaplon, and Fazio. If the observations are correct they obviously imply a remarkable situation, since no reasonable condition *associated with galaxies* can, it seems, produce such a result.

The place where the inverse Compton effect scores heavily over the synchrotron process is in the space between galaxies. We have already noticed that the intensity of starlight in extragalactic space is quite high. The magnetic field H, on the other hand, is probably rather low, say 10^{-8} gauss, so that H^2 falls by a factor 10^{-5} or so, as we pass from the interior of a galaxy to the space outside. Synchrotron radiation must therefore fall off very steeply, even if cosmic rays and electrons exist outside the galaxies with just as high an energy density as inside galaxies. The inverse Compton process only falls off by a moderate factor, however, say by 10^{-2}. Since the volume of space outside galaxies exceeds that inside galaxies by about 10^6, this means that the inverse Compton effect from the whole of space would exceed that from galaxies by as much as 10^4, *if the cosmic rays are everywhere the same.* This important point was made by Felten and Morrison.

The simplest procedure is to ask the direct question: What energy density of electrons is required to explain the presumed facts? Taking the intergalactic energy density of starlight as 10^{-14} erg per cm^3, the answer is about 2.10^{-15} erg per cm^3 if we accept the γ-ray value of Duthie, Hafner, Kaplon and Fazio, and about 4.10^{-16} erg per cm^3 if we accept the value of Kraushaar and Clark. This would apply to electrons with energies greater than one to two billion volts. The total necessary electron energy should be set quite approximately at 10^{-15} erg cm^{-3}. The last step is to multiply by 10^2 to obtain the proton energy, about 10^{-13} erg cm^{-3}, since on this picture we are arguing that the cosmic rays are the same everywhere, and the electron energy is only 1 per cent of the proton energy for the cosmic rays in the vicinity of the earth. This result, you notice, is consistent with our former estimate.

The importance of establishing a definitive result for the γ-ray flux over the energy range 10 to 100 million volts is obvious from this argument. Here we have one of the most critical observations of present-day astronomy. Depending on it, we may be able to establish whether cosmic rays are universal or not. Why make such a fuss about this problem? Because if cosmic rays are universal, high-energy particles and high-energy phenomena must play a critical role in controlling the local behaviour of the intergalactic medium. The problem of the formation and origin of galaxies would then be directly concerned with the distribution and origin of cosmic rays. One galaxy could affect others through the cosmic rays that it produced. There could be whole clusters dominated by some master galaxy, as observation suggests is actually the case. A wide range of questions, digging through to the mainspring of modern astronomy, turns on these problems of X rays, γ-rays and cosmic rays.

Bibliography of papers referred to in this chapter

V. L. GINZBURG and S. I. SYROVATSKY. *The Origin of Cosmic Rays*, Pergamon Press.

R. J. GOULD and G. R. BURBIDGE. "Symposium on Astronomical Observations from Space Vehicles," *Annales d'Astrophysique*, 1965.

G. R. BURBIDGE and F. HOYLE. *Nuovo Cimento*, Vol. 4, p. 1, 1956.

J. A. DESHONG JR., R. H. HILDEBRAND and P. MEYER. *Physical Review Letters*, Vol. 12, p. 3, 1964.

S. BOWYER, E. T. BRYAM, T. A. CHUBB and H. FRIEDMAN. *Nature*, Vol. 201, p. 1307, 1964.

R. GIACCONI, H. GURSKY, F. R. PAOLINI and B. B. ROSSI. *Physical Review Letters*, Vol. 9, p. 439, 1962.

J. E. Felten and P. Morrison. *Physical Review Letters*, Vol. 10, p. 453, 1963.

W. L. Kraushaar and G. W. Clark. *Physical Review Letters*, Vol. 8, p. 106, 1962.

J. G. Duthie, E. M. Hafner, M. F. Kaplon and G. G. Fazio. *Physical Review Letters*, Vol. 10, p. 364, 1963.

4

The Steady-State Cosmology

Not enough attention is paid in general terms to why so many scientific theories are put forward. To those not actively working in a particular field it is hard to appreciate how much can be said *in favor* of each of a number of mutually contradictory theories. Quick examination by the non-expert inevitably gives the impression of a confused situation, and indeed the layman can be excused for wondering how scientists can ever be sure of anything—justifiably sure, that is to say! Yet scientific evolution proceeds remorselessly; several theories may compete with each other for a while, but sooner or later all but one will fall by the wayside, leaving the victor, not necessarily "right," but at least surviving. What happens, you may wonder, when the balance shifts so that one theory comes more and more into favor while its rivals gently subside? What has happened to change the situation? If there was a good argument before to support a now-discarded theory, why isn't the argument still good?

There are at least three reasons for these shifts of emphasis.

The simplest possibility is that new data, or new arguments, come along that are far more decisive than any which existed previously. A good example in my own experience has been the highly controversial problem of the origin of the planets. According to quite early ideas, more than a century old, the planets were formed at the same time as the sun. Laplace even suggested that the planetary material might have quitted the sun because the latter was spinning very rapidly. But doubts were then cast on this idea, because if all the planets were dumped back into the sun, the sun would *not* spin fast enough to cause any rotational instability. This seemed to imply a contradiction in the old theory, and astronomers began to look for new ideas. The direction of investigation was toward multiple-star theories; the idea being that the planetary material came from another star, which at one time was a binary companion of the sun. Because there is no stellar companion of the sun at the present moment, it was necessary to get rid of the ultimately unwanted companion in some fashion. Various shifts were tried, including one that I proposed. I had gotten trapped into a wrong line of attack because this was the trend of research immediately prior to my own work.

What were the new facts or ideas that upset the apple cart? As the chemical composition of both the sun and the planets became better known, it at last became clear that although most of the planetary material, when lumped together, is hydrogen and helium, just as most of the material of the sun is hydrogen and helium, the hydrogen–helium excess in the planets is not nearly as marked as it is in the sun. More particularly, the hydrogen and helium constitute about 99 per cent of the sun but only about 90 per cent of the planetary material. So, if the planetary material came from the sun, as the early workers had suggested, a lot of hydrogen and helium must have evaporated out of it and must have been entirely lost from the solar system. A simple calculation along these lines shows that the present planets can have only one-tenth of the original amount of material. Hence the argument used some thirty or forty years ago—the argument about dumping the planets back in the sun, was not a fair argument. To carry the argument through consistently, it was necessary to allow for the escaping hydrogen and helium. When this was done it was found that dumping the *whole* planetary material back into the sun would indeed produce rotational instability. So an apparent contradiction to the general idea of the old theory was removed by a better knowledge of the chemical composition of the sun and planets. And other data of a different kind came along which also pointed back to the old theory. From an increased understanding of the manner of star formation, it became clear that the sun could not condense from the diffuse interstellar gas with a rotation as slow as we now find it to have. The primitive sun must have been spinning rapidly and some process must have occurred whereby the spin was reduced, demanding a transference of angular momentum. To what? Fairly obviously, to the planets just as Laplace suggested so long ago.

Another typical cause of trouble runs like this. We have two theories, A and B, dealing with some particular phenomenon. There is an instinctive preference for A by most workers in the field, but unfortunately A is directly contradicted by some observation or experiment, which points to the less-attractive B. So off we go on the trail of B, working out its consequences as best we can, only to find indifferent agreement with other experiments or observations, which may indeed have a better fit with A. Since neither theory works properly, we may feel tempted to look for a third theory, C. And at the end of it we may find that the critical observation that seemed to contradict A was just plain wrong, that *A* was right after all, and that we have been trapped into a lot of fruitless work by a wrong "fact."

Astronomy is particularly susceptible to this kind of difficulty. Once a wrong fact is suspected in an experimental science it is usually possible to change the original experiment, to do the experiment in a different way. This may not be possible in astronomy. We have to deal with an observation, not an experiment, and all that can be done is to repeat the observation. Frequently, the observation lies at the limit of instrumental capacity, and this only makes the situation worse. In the past, astronomy was more plagued by wrong facts than it is today, not because the inherent difficulties have been removed, but because astronomers are now very careful to put in question marks whenever observations are manifestly difficult and therefore potentially subject to error. The problem for the theoretician is not so much to avoid being mistakenly shoved onto a wrong track by some confidently asserted wrong fact, but to navigate safely through a mine field of question marks. This is particularly true of cosmology, the subject of the present chapter.

The third difficulty in theoretical work is entirely of the theoreticians' own making. You are trying to find a theory of a certain phenomenon, and you can see that there are several possibilities *A, B, C, ...* Systematically, you set about investigating them in turn, with a view to finding which gives the best fit to the facts. You make a start on *A.* Soon, however, you run into the trouble that *A* is not a simple straight road. It has forking points. At the first such point you have to cope with, say, two possibilities, *A*/1 and *A*/2. Then as you follow these you find further alternatives, and so on. Rapidly the possibilities multiply up and soon you feel that a completely systematic investigation of them all is going to take far too long, that you are never going to *reach* B, still less C. If we were dealing only in logic, the right thing to do would be to subdivide the problem among all the available workers. But human nature being what it is, this just won't work. We would each feel that the right answer might not lie in our particular subdivision and we would be resentful of being prevented from thinking about the other possibilities. So the tendency is for each worker to attempt to cover all the possibilities for himself. Manifestly, he must look for shortcuts.

A tempting, but not satisfactory, method of shortcutting is that of choosing the "most probable" alternative at each of the forking points. The facts, together with previous experience, often suggest that $A/1$ is more likely to be right than $A/2$. It is then all too easy to continue the exploration of $A/1$, but to ignore $A/2$. A trivial calculation soon exposes the unsoundness of this procedure. First, suppose theory A happens to be "right." Suppose you judge the possibility of $A/1$ to be three times that of $A/2$, ¾ for $A/1$ and ¼ for $A/2$. And suppose ten such alternatives present themselves, each with a three to one probability. So you end up with a theory that has a probability $(¾)^{10}$ of being the correct one, i.e., a chance of only about one in twenty! Although you have investigated what appears to be the most likely theory, the possibilities that you have not investigated *when taken together* are far more likely to contain the required answer than your one single investigation. The situation is that instinct and prejudice, as to which of two alternatives seems the more "probable," often turn out to be wrong. Our attempts to anticipate nature in this way turn out poorly. Indeed, it is easy to be entirely misled. By doing the same thing also for theories B, C . . . we arrive at "most probable" lines of investigation for B, C, ... Then we proceed to compare the single lines for all of A, B, C. . . . It may appear that the investigation for C, say, looks better—seems to fit the facts better—than the investigation for A, because we have missed the right line for A through our "probability" procedure. Hence we may be led completely onto the wrong track. So quite wrong theories may come to be preferred to what finally emerges as the right one—when someone at last takes the trouble to make a complete investigation of the right theory, or is lucky enough to stumble on the right path through the forking points.

There is, of course, no completely safe system of short-cutting. If there was, the job of the theoretician would be much easier than it actually is. Inevitably one must abandon most of the alternatives one investigates, and it is the process of rejection on which everything hangs. Some skill and a lot of luck are needed if you are to avoid throwing away rough diamonds along with the rest of the rubble.

There is no problem in astronomy in which these considerations are of more relevance than that of cosmology, the study of the whole universe. More factors enter this problem than any other, a wider range of observation and the full panoply of physics. Many theories have to be considered, and there are so many alternatives to be investigated within each one that some astronomers and physicists are inclined to dismiss cosmology as a hopeless subject of study. By this, I suppose, it is meant that we are so unlikely to find a satisfactory theory that there is little point in making the effort. Even if it is true that we are unlikely to find a satisfactory theory, I believe that we must still make the effort. Otherwise the philosophy of ignoring cosmology could persist indefinitely, and could impede progress should progress become possible in the future. At all times one must try for the best theory one can make, without presuming that the best theory of the present-day will seem the best theory a hundred years from now.

First, let us begin with the familiar fact that in *any locality* the number of ways in which a given quantity of energy can be distributed tends to increase with time. Start with most of your energy in a single particle. At a later time you will find part of the energy, perhaps most of it, has become shared with other particles. This concept can be applied to all forms of energy, in particular to the energy of mass of the particles. If you start with a simple mixture of electrons and protons, then change some of the electron–proton pairs into neutrino–neutron pairs, and combine protons and neutrons into nuclei, you can produce a reduction of mass, by nearly as much as 1 per cent. This is the process on which stars operate, and that governs the evolution of stars, which I shall be discussing in Chapter 6. For the moment, I simply want to notice that natural physical processes, if left to themselves for an indefinitely long period of time under the conditions we observe at the present-day, would lead to a situation in which simple mixtures of protons and electrons ceased to exist. In more explicit terms, such a mixture would form itself, sooner or later, into stars, and nuclear processes would destroy the free protons, building them into heavier nuclei. From the observation that most of the matter of the universe is hydrogen, a one-to-one electron–proton mixture, we can conclude that things cannot have been the way we now observe them to be for an indefinitely long time.

Three alternatives arise:

(1) that the laws of physics were not the same in the past as they are now;
(2) that the universe came into being a finite time ago;
(3) that the distribution of matter in the universe has not always been the same as it is now.

Here the road divides into a threefold prong. Most workers reject (1) out of hand, almost entirely without investigation. I am not convinced about this, for reasons that I will touch on in Chapter 6. However, it should be said that you cannot be as free in changing the laws of physics as might be thought at first sight. Light from distant galaxies takes several billion years to reach us. From spectroscopic examination of the light, information about the laws that governed its emission *billions of years* ago can be obtained. Such information is entirely consistent with the laws being then the same as they are at the present. Furthermore, the decay of naturally radioactive materials gives information about the past history of the earth and of meteorites. The relevant physical processes for the decay of uranium on the one hand, and for the decay of Rb^{87} on the other hand, are quite different. Yet both processes point to the same past history, again suggesting that the laws have not changed significantly over periods of several billion years.

Possibility (2) has achieved wide discussion because the concept of a world with beginning but without end is a part of Judaism and of the derivative Christian culture. The reason why the concepts of finiteness and of infinity became so intertwined with these cultures is, presumably, that man happened to be grappling with the intellectual problem of infinity during the epoch in which these religions were invented. Because infinity was regarded as the most subtle of current ideas, it got itself mixed into the brew, along with notions of ethics, law, and other intellectual concepts, including the cosmology of the day. But unless you are willing to contemplate a universe *without beginning,* yet with an end, there is nothing in this for you. The two descriptions: universe with beginning, but without end, and universe with end, but without beginning, are identical, as can be seen from simply inverting the sense of time. What I am saying is that one cannot have a strong emotional preference for the first of these without *either* having a similar strong preference for the second *or* of being guilty of an error of logic.

The third alternative leads to a remarkable success. Suppose we inquire how, in the large, the material of the universe might move consistent with two requirements:

(i) There should be no privileged position in the universe, no center, no place where things look any different from any other place.

(ii) From your own position things look the same in all directions.

It turns out that these conditions of homogeneity and isotropy place strong restrictions on the possible motions. Imagine the particles of matter—the galaxies can be considered as particles for this purpose—to be connected by rods. Then the galaxies and their connecting rods make up a lattice analogous to a crystal lattice. This refers to any particular moment of time. As time changes, our restrictions require the shape of the lattice to stay the same. All that can change are the lengths of the imaginary connecting rods. The *scale* of the lattice can change but not its shape. Three galaxies, for example, form a triangle, which will maintain the same shape at all times. Hence we can specify the state of the universe at any given moment simply by giving the current value of the scale of the lattice, $S(t)$ where t is the time.

From the theory of relativity, important information can be obtained about the way that S varies with t. However, once again we have a forking point, there are several possibilities. Three cases, marked 0, ½, 1, are shown in Figure 2.

There are other possibilities that are not so much in line with current orthodox views, and that are not shown in Figure 2. From these results it is possible to predict how galaxies should be observed to move, the predictions being shown in Figure 1 on page 21 (the cases zero and +1 of Figure 1 being the same as those of Figure 2). As explained in connection with Figure 1, the vertical scale is a measure of the red shift of spectrum lines. *It is the red shift that is actually predicted.*

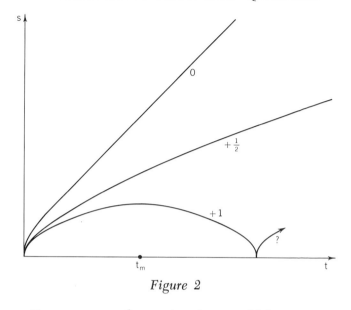

Figure 2

By motion, we mean the motion that would be necessary to produce the same red shift in the laboratory. The horizontal scale of Figure 1 is a measure of distance, provided all galaxies have the same intrinsic emission.

The modern data, taken at face value, fit the $+1$ curve of Figure 1 very well. However, the different curves of Figure 1 are not very widely spaced, and allowance for distant galaxies having somewhat different intrinsic emissions has suggested more a fit to $+\frac{1}{2}$, or even to the zero curve.

For smaller distances all cases give the same curve, a straight line. The fact that galaxies are observed to cluster about this line represents perhaps the most solid achievement of theoretical cosmology. It points strongly toward the correctness of the restrictions (i) and (ii) set out above. However, a puzzling situation has arisen. It can be seen from Figure 2 that if we follow time back to a certain moment ($t = 0$ in Figure 2) we have $S = 0$. The scale factor of the lattice decreases to zero, and all particles separated at present by finite distances come together. The density of matter therefore becomes infinite.

How long ago was this singular situation? By a combination of theory and observation we arrive at nearly 9 billion years for the $+\frac{1}{2}$ case, at about 13 billion years for the zero case, and at about 7 billion years for the $+1$ case. From quite independent astrophysical calculations, the best estimate for the age of our Galaxy is from 10 to 15 billion years. The zero case and the $+\frac{1}{2}$ case can be reconciled with this requirement, but the situation for the $+1$ case is rather doubtful.

On the other hand, the $+1$ case offers a hope of avoiding a serious logical difficulty contained in the other cases. The curve of $S(t)$ for the $+1$ case has the form of a hoop. The scale factor decreases after reaching a maximum value at $t = t_m$. It decreases back to zero at $t = 2t_m$. The literal interpretation of this result is that the universe comes into being at $t = 0$ and goes out of existence at $t = 2t_m$. We can attempt to evade this conclusion, however, by arguing that S does not decrease absolutely to zero, that S decreases to some minimum value, after which it increases again. Then the behavior of the scale factor would follow a sequence of hoops,

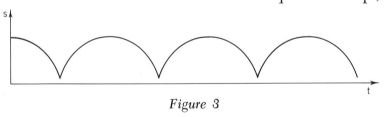

Figure 3

as in Figure 3. In this case we can have a universe not only without end, but without beginning. The universe oscillates periodically in a cycle time of $2t_m$.

A somewhat similar idea could be used for the other cases, but seems rather artificial. We could argue, both for the zero case and the $+\frac{1}{2}$ case, that we have the situation of Figure 4. It is immaterial in which sense we elect to measure time from the point of symmetry, which is chosen as $t = 0$ in Figure 4. On one side of Figure 4 the universe contracts, on the other side it expands, so we have a picture of a universe that shrinks from a state of infinite dispersal, the shrinkage going on until a certain, as yet undetermined, minimum value of S is reached. Thereafter the shrinkage is replaced by expansion, and the universe goes back to its state of infinite dispersal.

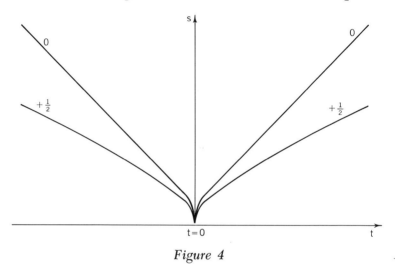

Figure 4

It is possible to subject the oscillating model of Figure 3 to a rather stringent test, out of which it comes with a good deal of credit. Clearly, galaxies and stars must be destroyed at the moments of high density, otherwise there would be a steady conversion of material into stars as we proceed from cycle to cycle, and hydrogen would be steadily converted inside stars into heavier elements. After a sufficient number of cycles all hydrogen would be gone, which contradicts observation. This is avoided if the temperature is high enough at the moments of high density. Then the galaxies and stars evaporate, the matter becoming a hot cloud of gas. At a sufficiently high temperature it can be shown that physical processes require the matter to be an almost equal mixture of protons and neutrons. After the turnabout as S begins to increase, the temperature falls. Neutrons disappear, partly by free decay, partly by combining with the protons to form helium. It turns out that the whole business can be subject to rather precise calculation, and the outcome is a mixture of hydrogen and helium, in a ratio (by mass) of about 2:1. This result is independent of the physical conditions within quite a wide range, provided only that the temperature goes high enough. Now the hydrogen to helium ratio observed in the sun, the stars, the interstellar gas (both of our own Galaxy and of several nearby galaxies) is indeed about 2:1. The agreement is very striking, although strict attention to detail reveals discrepancies; the currently estimated helium content of the sun, for example, is lower than the calculated value by about 40 per cent. However, helium is a difficult element to observe, and the current estimates might be in error by this amount.

The really remarkable point emerges that a sample of a pint of solar material, if only we could get hold of it, could disprove the oscillating cosmology of Figure 3. In the absence of such a sample we can only mark down this result as a success for the oscillating theory, pointing in the opposite direction to the age difficulty mentioned above.

The equations determining the behavior of S show that in the +1 case there must be a maximum value of S, that expansion must cease at a certain stage and be followed by contraction. But the equations do not show the opposite case, of why there should be a minimum value of S, that contraction must cease and be followed by expansion. Indeed, so long as we stick to the restrictions (i) and (ii) of page 89, which you remember led to the success in explaining the observational data of Figure 1, there can be no switch from contraction to expansion in this theory.

It is possible to argue that while restrictions (i) and (ii) apply in a good approximation at the present time, they did not apply near the time of switch from contraction to expansion. The possibility of dropping (ii) but not (i) has been investigated in some detail. It does not seem to improve the situation. Much work remains to be done before a final opinion emerges on the effect of dropping (i), however. A less difficult but similar problem concerns the gravitational collapse of a local object, the problem that has been considered in some detail in connection with the quasi-stellar radio sources. It is well known that all investigations so far, based on the usual theory, have run into difficulties connected exactly with this same problem of "bounce," of switch from contraction to expansion. So far, a switch has not been found, even for a local object.

At this point it is necessary for the theoretician to decide whether he wishes to persist along the lines indicated above by investigating more and more complex possibilities, or whether the stage has been reached at which quite new ideas should be explored. Three factors have to be considered

(a) Agreement with the empirical facts of observation.

(b) Reluctance to introduce concepts that have not come out of experimental investigations in the laboratory.

(c) The failure of orthodox cosmologies to come to grips with certain facts, which although observational are of apparently greater fundamental importance than the facts appearing under category (a).

There is a story that the late Wolfgang Pauli once interrupted a speaker, who had just used the word "fundamental," with the remark, "that is philosophy, and therefore nonsense." So I had better explain what I mean by a fact under (a) and a fact under (c). The precise positions where the observed galaxies fall in a plot of the type shown in Figure 1 would be a fact under (a). Such a fact arouses no emotional response. We accept it simply for what it is. Under (c), I would class the observed asymmetry of time, the fact that events occur in chains that are not symmetrical with respect to past and future. Notice I am not just playing with words here. It is always quite trivial, as I remarked above, to invert the meaning of past and future. Instead of saying that "I was born in the past and will die in the future," one could equally say "I was born in the future and will die in the past." The only difference here is a mathematical inversion of the sense of time, obtained by writing $-t$ everywhere in one's equations where previously one had used t. What is not trivial is that the trend from birth to death, whichever way one elects to describe it, is the same for all animals, the same as for the passage of an inorganic fuel to ashes.

The direction in which one elects to go seems to me to depend on the relative emotional strengths of (b) and (c). I am more swayed by (c) than by (b), because (c) weighs heavily with me, while (b) does not—I do not happen to believe that all of physics is discoverable in a terrestrial laboratory. I think many of my colleagues feel the opposite way. While very few physicists would perhaps be disposed to argue that all is discoverable in the laboratory, many would assert that the only certain knowledge is that which is discovered in the laboratory. The example of gravitation shows that this need not be the case. A more tenable point of view is that one should not depart from what is known in the laboratory until all possibilities consistent with laboratory knowledge have been fully investigated. The difficulty here is that no theory can ever be said to be "fully investigated." It is always possible to go on working away at more and more complicated cases. Judgment is needed as to when the moment has been reached for a breakaway from the orthodox pattern of thought. Plainly, not everybody will take the same view in making such a judgment, just because each person weighs the conflicting elements in a problem according to their own predilections.

Speaking personally now, I have a strong emotional dislike for special setups in cosmology. I can see that the oscillating cosmology might have been "initially" set up to give the observed asymmetry òf time, but any suggestion of "initial" tinkering being necessary to explain the most everyday features of our existence seems intensely distasteful to me. It implies that the universe is a poor sort of thing, only capable of lumbering along as a working concern if special adjustments are made, like the old car I used to run in the immediate postwar years. The idea I use in cosmological investigations is that all important aspects of the universe are contained within the laws, they are not impressed from outside the laws. This is one of the shortcuts I use. I personally spend no time investigating theories that require special initial conditions.

With the exception of a recent, still unresolved, problem concerning the decay of the K_2^0 meson, the laws of physics are believed to be time symmetric. How could time asymmetry arise from the operation of time symmetric laws? In Figure 5 we have a time symmetric situation, indicated schematically, symmetric about a particular point on the axis of time, which for convenience I have chosen to be $t = 0$. Since an arbitrary moment of time is not likely to be at all close to $t = 0$, such a moment will lie far to the right or far to the left. An observer living at such a moment will find his neighborhood to have a time asymmetry, but the asymmetry will be different according to whether the observer lies to the right of $t = 0$, or to the left.

Figure 5 shows how the problem of time asymmetry might

be solved in principle, although, of course, this does not prove the actual existence of such a scheme. It shows that the problem is not a hopeless one, and also what one might aim for. Referring back to Figure 4, we have indeed a similar situation with respect to the behavior of the scale factor $S(t)$. Hence the cosmologies of Figure 4 have more potentiality for an understanding of the asymmetry of time than has the cosmology of Figure 3. When one examines details, difficulties

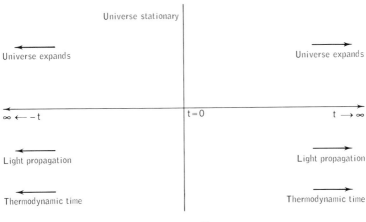

Figure 5

appear, however. It does not seem as if the asymmetric sense of light propagation can be explained, for example. The same difficulty concerning the bounce at $t = 0$ applies also, exactly as in the switches from contraction to expansion in the oscillating cosmology.

In the previous chapter I drew attention to the remarkable point that the universe does not consist of equal quantities of matter and antimatter, unless one supposes that the two kinds of matter exist in well-separated blobs, a separation that is very difficult to explain. If we reject the blob idea as too artificial, we are faced by the necessity *either* to break the laboratory rule that baryons and anti-baryons are always created in equal numbers *or* the origin of matter is beyond the range of physical explanation. The second alternative would seem to lead inevitably to the cosmologies described above, and to the still unsolved problem of how the universe can switch from contraction to expansion. The first alternative leads to a quite new alternative, which I shall describe in the remainder of this chapter.

The idea that each particle of matter might have had a separate origin leads to the concept of the steady-state universe. Expansion of the universe must cause the density of matter to fall as time goes on, unless new matter appears, in which case it would be possible for the effect of expansion to be compensated by the effect of "creation." The distances between the galaxies increase with the expansion, so that the density of galaxies must also lessen unless new galaxies are constantly being formed from newly created material. This new concept of a steady-state universe leads, therefore, to the requirement that new galaxies form all the time. It was to test this requirement that the investigation of peculiar galaxies, described in the first chapter, was carried out. The general outcome of this investigation was that the data are consistent with the requirement, although the formation of new galaxies was not considered to be proven.

The steady-state concept, as a strict precept, is at variance with the counts of radio sources by Ryle and Clarke. The data show that radio sources were either systematically more frequent, more powerful, or both, in the past than they are at present. A possibility for modifying the strict steady-state idea was discussed by Narlikar and myself. Although we were able to obtain agreement with the data, I think that we would now much prefer the development that I shall be describing later in Chapter 5.

Reference back to Figure 1 shows a curve marked −1. This is the predicted curve for the steady-state theory. Because the most distant galaxies probably fall between the zero case and case +1 this is another piece of data against the steady-state theory. However, the discrepancy in this case is not very great and can perhaps be regarded as within the uncertainty of the data.

Putting aside the steady-state concept *as a precept,* how can such a theory be described in mathematical terms? A new field is required, which may be referred to as the C-field, a field that acts on a particle, or particles, at the moment of its

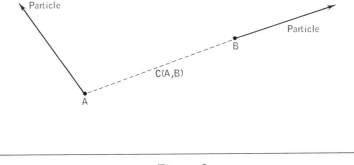

Figure 6

(their) origin. We can think of a particle as a line in the four dimensions of space and time. The origin of a particle is represented as a line with a beginning, the destruction of a particle by a line with an end, as in Figure 6. The roles of creation and destruction can be inverted by switching the sense of t. Evidently, then, I am not emphasizing creation as opposed to annihilation, but rather that there can be termination points to the lines represented by particles. The C-field operates at the termination points. There would be a coupling between the termination points of particles A and B in Figure 6, marked as C(A,B).

The C-field propagates in space–time in the same way as all other fields that satisfy the "wave equation." The total C-field at an arbitrary point X is just the sum of all the contributions from all termination points, as shown schematically in Figure 7. If this total C-field carries sufficient energy, it is possible for a new particle, or particles, to appear at X. The requirement on the energy is just that the C-field energy must be at least as great as the mass of the created particle (or particles). The momentum of the created particle(s) is equal to that carried by the C-field, so that momentum and

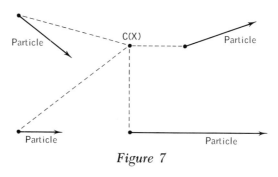

Figure 7

energy are rigorously conserved in the creation process, and also, of course, in the corresponding annihiliation process.

With all this expressed by mathematical equations, it is possible to examine the consequences of the creation/annihilation of matter. The simplest case to treat is that in which the restrictions (i) and (ii) of page 89 continue to hold. Indeed these restrictions lead to a completely unique solution. It has the interesting symmetry shown in Figure 8, a symmetry of the kind required to give the situation already discussed in connection with Figure 5. We now have the additional feature that the termination points of the particles are also symmetrically disposed with respect to the moment of symmetry, which again I have denoted by $t = 0$. If you make the rule that time is to be measured always in a sense *away from this moment of symmetry*, then the universe expands both as time progresses to the right in Figure 8, and as it progresses to the left. Particles are created only, when time is read in this way. However, if we regard time as advancing from left to right, on both sides of $t = 0$, the universe contracts to the left of $t = 0$ and particles are annihilated, while the universe expands to the right of $t = 0$ and particles are created. These statements are inverted if we elect to read time from right to left.

What is the sense in which light travels? Narlikar and I have investigated this problem. We have shown that the directions of travel given in Figure 5 are consistent solutions of our equations. It seems likely that the opposite direction of travel, i.e., travel toward $t = 0$, is not consistent with the equations, although we have not yet been able to give a complete proof of this.

An interesting feature of Figure 8 is that by considering the creation/annihilation only of particles, not of antiparticles, we still obtain a double world, one to the right of $t = 0$, the

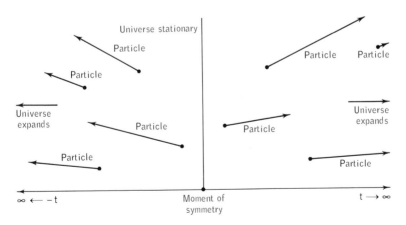

Figure 8

other to the left of $t = 0$. My statement that we are only dealing in particles, not antiparticles, applies for the case in which we read time the same way on both sides of $t = 0$, e.g., from left to right. But if we read time always in a sense away from $t = 0$ we must make a switch at $t = 0$ in meaning of particles and antiparticles. Reading time away from $t = 0$, the world to the right of $t = 0$ can be a world of matter; the world to the left of $t = 0$ is then a world of antimatter. This is not just a play on words. Provided the senses of light propagation, and the senses of propagation of other fields, also switch between $t \to \infty$ and $-t \to \infty$, experiments in the world to the right of $t = 0$ would yield an opposite helicity (e.g., in the well-known Co^{60} experiment) from that to the left of $t = 0$.

The unique cosmology (obtained from the mathematical equations incorporating the C-field and using the restrictions (i) and (ii), page 89 of homogeneity and isotropy), is not strictly a steady-state cosmology. This is shown by the fact that the universe is neither expanding nor contracting at the moment of time symmetry, $t = 0$. However, an observer living at a random moment of time is most unlikely to be near the point of time symmetry. He will live either far away to the right, $t \to \infty$, or far away to the left, $-t \to \infty$. And the solution of the equations far away to the right or to the left is the solution of steady-state cosmology. The density of matter in space tends to a steady value, for instance. The scale factor S follows a curve of the kind shown in Figure 9.

Although the cosmology is unique, under the conditions just stated, it contains an uncertainty that will become important in the next chapter. The coupling of the C-field to the termination points of particles is the critical postulate on which the theory is based. Because this coupling is *postulated* we do not know its strength. It could be zero, in which case we would be back at the old cosmologies discussed

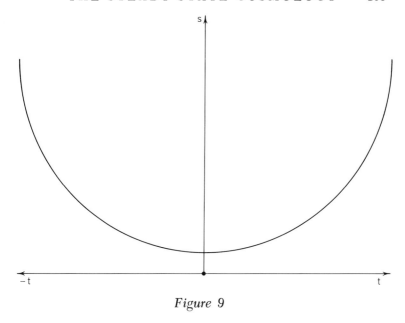

Figure 9

earlier in this chapter. Provided the coupling is not zero, however, we arrive at the theory just described. The strength of the coupling is decided by one number, which we may denote by f. This number determines the density of matter—the density for large t or large —t is simply proportional to f; in fact, units of measurement can be chosen such that the density, denoted by ρ, is just f itself, either for large t or large —t ($\rho \to f$ as $|t| \to \infty$). Then the density at $t = 0$ is ½ f, so that the density is not strictly the same at all times. It has a steady value when we are not near the point of time symmetry. However, the density fluctuates only between ½ f and f, and is not subject to the very large variations that occur in other cosmologies, which give ρ proportional to the inverse cube of S, $\rho \propto S^{-3}$.

As I say, we have no *a priori* knowledge of the value of f. It is natural, therefore, to look for some way of fixing f by a reference to observation. This has been done in the following way. The vertical scale of Figure 9 also depends on f. By taking different values of f we obtain different curves, as in Figure 10.

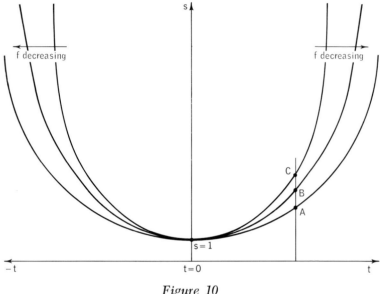

Figure 10

All curves have been given the same value at t = 0. We are free to do this because S, you will recall, is simply a lattice scale factor, and we can always choose our unit of length measurement so that S has any assigned value at any particular time, say S = 1 at t = 0, as in Figure 10. Next, fix a particular moment of time and draw a vertical line for that moment. The line will cut the different S curves at points . . . A, B, C, . . ., etc. It is seen from a trivial inspection of Figure 10 that the *slopes* of the S curves are different at these different points, and the slope of the S curve affects our observations of distant galaxies in the following way.

Turn back to Figure 1, page 21. You recall that the curves drawn in this figure represent the predicted dependence of the red shift of spectrum lines on distance. More precisely, we have the logarithm of the red shift $\Delta\lambda/\lambda$ as the ordinate axis, and a quantity that depends on the logarithm of distance as the abscissa, as in Figure 11. Provided we are not concerned with very big distances, the predicted curve in Figure 11 is

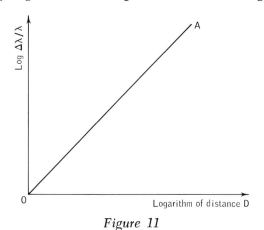

Figure 11

a straight line sloping upwards at 45°, like the line OA. However, it is possible to draw an infinity of lines parallel to OA, a few possibilities being shown in Figure 12. Which of these lines does the theory require us to choose? The answer depends on the slope of the S curve of Figure 10, and this in turn depends on the value we choose for our coupling constant f. Now we do not know f, so we must invert the procedure of comparing theory to observation. We must start with the observed nearby galaxies and see which of our family of parallel lines they happen to lie on, as in Figure 12, where the galaxies have been shown illustratively as falling on the fourth line. We then see what slope of the S curve is needed to obtain this fourth line, and finally we infer the appropriate value of f. This is the procedure by which the theory has been made determinate in the past. In the next chapter I shall be describing a very different method of coming to grips with the value of f.

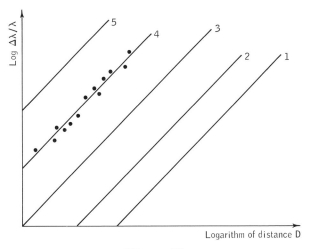

Figure 12

It remains for us to notice a few numerical values. With f determined in the manner I have just indicated, the density of matter in space is about 10^{-29} gm cm^{-3}. This is more than ten times the density that would be obtained if all the material of the galaxies were spread uniformly throughout space. Hence the theory requires that most of the material of the universe is not in the galaxies we observe, suggesting that ample material may exist in extragalactic regions wherewith to form new galaxies.

At an earlier stage I pointed out that the vertical scale of Figure 1, when interpreted as a *velocity scale*, must be treated with some caution. All we really measure is the red shift of spectrum lines, shown schematically in Figure 13. Here we have five lines a,b,c,d,e measured at wavelengths λ_a, λ_b, λ_c, λ_d,

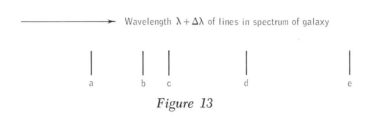

Figure 13

λ_e in the laboratory. The same five lines appear in the spectrum of a galaxy, but now at wavelengths $\lambda_a + \Delta\lambda_a$, $\lambda_b + \Delta\lambda_b$, $\lambda_c + \Delta\lambda_c$, $\lambda_d + \Delta\lambda_d$, $\lambda_e + \Delta\lambda_e$. How do we know them to be the same lines? Because their ratios are the same—

$$\lambda_a + \Delta\lambda_a : \lambda_b + \Delta\lambda_b : \lambda_c + \Delta\lambda_c : \lambda_d + \Delta\lambda_d : \lambda_e + \Delta\lambda_e$$
$$= \lambda_a : \lambda_b : \lambda_c : \lambda_d : \lambda_e$$

i.e., $\dfrac{\Delta\lambda_a}{\lambda_a} = \dfrac{\Delta\lambda_b}{\lambda_b} = \dfrac{\Delta\lambda_c}{\lambda_c} = \dfrac{\Delta\lambda_d}{\lambda_d} = \dfrac{\Delta\lambda_e}{\lambda_e} = \dfrac{\Delta\lambda}{\lambda}$.

This is the quantity $\Delta\lambda/\lambda$ plotted in our previous figures. This is what we get from observation. There is no velocity measurement. Then where does velocity come in? How is it that we often talk about the speeds of recession of the galaxies?

In the laboratory it is found that spectrum lines in the light from a receding object have increased wavelengths, and that $\Delta\lambda/\lambda$ has the same value for all lines, exactly the same as for the galaxies. When we speak about the velocity of a galaxy we mean the velocity of a laboratory light source that would give the same $\Delta\lambda/\lambda$ as is observed for the galaxy in question.

The relation between $\Delta\lambda/\lambda$ and velocity, for a laboratory source of light, is shown in Figure 14. The curve starts by going up at 45°, but then steepens as the velocity increases, so that $\Delta\lambda/\lambda \rightarrow \infty$ as the velocity of light is approached. This behavior causes a real confusion if we continue to apply

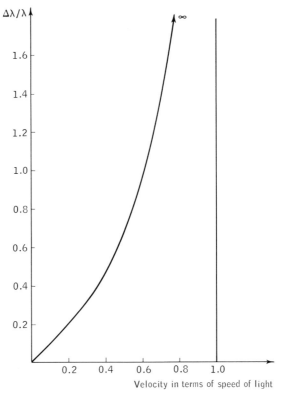

Figure 14

the velocity concept to galaxies as $\Delta\lambda/\lambda$ becomes large. So long as we are on the 45° degree part of Figure 14 it is, of course, immaterial whether we elect to speak about the actually observed $\Delta\lambda/\lambda$, or the equivalent laboratory velocity. But as the infinity in $\Delta\lambda/\lambda$ is approached no purpose, except that of causing confusion, is served by this procedure. It is better to stick to the relation between $\Delta\lambda/\lambda$ and distance, as in Figure 12. The straight-line relationship between log $\Delta\lambda/\lambda$ and log D, D the distance, shown in Figure 12, applies only for nearby galaxies—that is to say, for galaxies that have values of $\Delta\lambda/\lambda$ much smaller than unity. How does the curve go when $\Delta\lambda/\lambda$ becomes large?

The answer to this interesting question depends on what cosmology we are dealing with. All cosmologies give the 45° line of Figure 12 when $\Delta\lambda/\lambda$ is small, but differences occur when $\Delta\lambda/\lambda$ is large, as indeed is already seen in Figure 1, page 21. In Figure 15 I have sketched the dependence of $\Delta\lambda/\lambda$ on distance for the steady-state cosmology (i.e., t not near the moment of time symmetry), and also the dependence for the $+\frac{1}{2}$ cosmology. The latter is illustrative of the situation for the cosmologies discussed earlier in this chapter, the $+\frac{1}{2}$ cosmology being that of Einstein and de Sitter.

Before we discuss these curves, the meaning of D needs emphasis. D is the present distance. Suppose that you could instantaneously measure the distance of a galaxy, for example with the aid of a ruler. This would be D. The interesting point emerges that, while the 45° slope continues indefinitely for the steady-state theory, for the $+\frac{1}{2}$ cosmology the red shift $\Delta\lambda/\lambda$ tends to infinity at a certain finite value of D. Galaxies at a greater value of D cannot be observed at all. What determines this value of D? The present epoch. An observer who drew a similar curve in the future would find the 45° slope to extend to a greater distance. He would also find that the turn-up with $\Delta\lambda/\lambda \to \infty$ occurred at larger D. The curve for the steady-state cosmology stays the same, however, as t increases.

The curve for the $+\frac{1}{2}$ cosmology has a similar shape to that of the laboratory dependence of red shift on velocity, (Figure 14). If we like we can interpret this similarity, *in a*

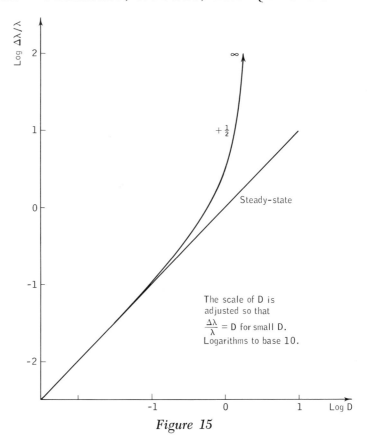

Figure 15

purely formal way, by saying that the recessional velocity of a galaxy at the limiting value of D for the $+\frac{1}{2}$ cosmology goes to the speed of light. But no such interpretation can be given for the steady-state theory.

Once again it must be emphasized that all this refers to the practical situation, to the light that we are now receiving with actual telescopes. The $+\frac{1}{2}$ cosmology says that present-day observation must be restricted to light from galaxies whose present-day distances do not exceed a certain maximum value. The steady-state theory permits us to be receiving light from galaxies with arbitrarily large values of D. Suppose now we set up a quite different problem. Suppose we concern ourselves with light emitted by galaxies at the present day, which will be received by an observer in our galaxy at some time in the future. What is the relation between the present-day D and the future-time T at which the light reaches us; T = 0 at the present day. The results for the two cosmologies are shown in Figure 16. Exactly the reverse situation now appears.

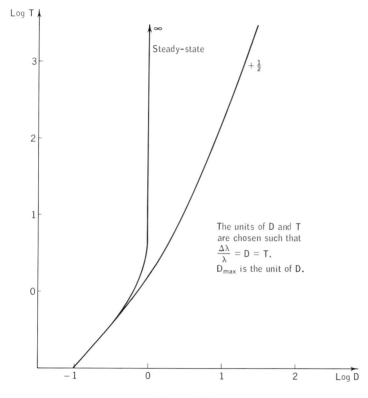

Figure 16

A maximum distance exists for the steady-state theory but not for the $+\frac{1}{2}$ theory. No matter how long our observer in this Galaxy waits, he can never observe signals emitted *at the present day* from a galaxy with present-day distance greater than D_{max}, according to the steady-state theory. For the value of f chosen in the way described above, D_{max} turns out to be about 10,000 million light-years, or about 10^{28}cm. This limiting distance is often referred to as the radius of the "observable universe." The mass within the observable universe is easily obtained by multiplying $4\pi D_{max}^3/3$ by the density, about 10^{-29} gm. It is nearly 10^{56}gm, about 10^{23} times the mass of the sun, and is sometimes spoken of as the mass of the observable universe. However, it is important to realize that this applies to the future, to what happens from here on.

Keeping clearly in mind that Figures 15 and 16 refer to two quite different problems (Figure 15 to light that was emitted in the past and which is now being received, Figure 16 to the future), it is evidently possible to observe galaxies, or other objects, that now lie beyond the radius of the observable universe, i.e., from which no future signals will ever be reached—all this on the steady-state theory of course. Suppose we take the distance D_{max} in Figure 16 and read off the corresponding value of $\Delta\lambda/\lambda$ from Figure 15. Then we know that any object for which the red shift is greater than this lies *now* outside the observable universe. The appropriate value turns out to have a pleasing simplicity, just $\Delta\lambda/\lambda = 1$.

Recently, quasars with $\Delta\lambda/\lambda$ greater than unity have been observed by Schmidt. If the red shifts are of cosmological origin, these objects lie beyond D_{max}. One of Schmidt's earlier determinations, the quasar 3C 147, is shown in Plate XXXII. For 3C 147, $\Delta\lambda/\lambda = 0.545$, so this object has a present-day value of D given by $D = 0.545\ D_{max}$, if the red shift is of cosmological origin.

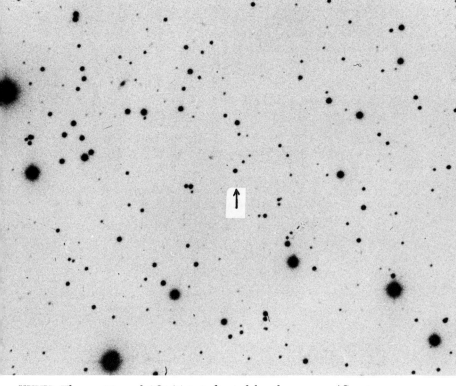

XXXII. The position of 3C147 is indicated by the arrow. (Courtesy M. Schmidt, California Institute of Technology.)

To end this chapter, I would like to come back to item (c) of page 94. These were the facts that I regarded as more "fundamental" than direct empirical facts, such as the star content of a particular galaxy. I gave the common experience of the asymmetry of time as an example of a fundamental fact. Another deep-rooted aspect of the universe is implicit in the whole of the above discussion, in the use made of the concept of simultaneity. The distance D is the present-day distance, implying that the present day has physical meaning over the whole of the route from us to the galaxy in question; the route along which we imagined laying our ruler. Simultaneity can always be given a purely geometrical significance, simply from the choice of coordinates. The surprise is finding simultaneity playing a critical physical role throughout cosmology.

It is not difficult to see where simultaneity was introduced into our physical picture—by the restriction (i) on page 89. The concept of different places being indistinguishable from each other implies simultaneity, since in a nonstatic universe the different places must be considered *at the same time*. Restriction (i) does not necessarily apply to observers at different places if the times are different. The surprising thing is that the restriction works, it leads to the linear relation between $\Delta\lambda/\lambda$ and D for galaxies that are not too distant, and this agrees with observation, an agreement which I described as the most solid achievement of cosmology. Now we see that this achievement rests on simultaneity having physical importance. Time and space assume much the same roles that they have in Newtonian physics. Indeed, it can be said that the reason why Newtonian physics gives a satisfactory description of the world, up to a point, is because it deals largely in phenomena that are controlled by the cosmological situation.

The theory of relativity tells us that special coordinate systems, special choices for measuring time and space, can have no importance so far as the laws of physics are concerned. The laws work equally well for any one of an infinity of choices for the coordinates. How then can the laws ever lead to one particular system of coordinates, and have the dominating importance that we apparently find in cosmology? The relativity theory tells us that the behavior of a physical system can be worked out equally well in any of an infinite set of possible choices for the space and time coordinates.

The system will "do the same thing" irrespective of the co-ordinates we happen to choose for the purpose of calculation. However, the relativity theory does not tell us that the calculation will be equally easy to work out for all choices of the coordinates. For one choice the calculation may be compara-tively straightforward, and for others it may be much more complicated. And this is exactly the situation in cosmology. The calculation leading to Figure 1, for instance, could have been performed for other systems of space and time, the essential physical results would have been the same, but much harder to arrive at.

So you ask: What makes the calculation easier in one sys-tem than in others? What makes restriction (i) particularly easy to understand, and elegant in its statement, for the Newtonian-like space–time system used throughout the above discussion? The relativity theory offers no help here, and the usual supposition of cosmology is that the simplicity in ques-tion is a reflection of the manner in which the universe was set up in the first place. Back to first causes, the philosophy that I objected to so strenuously before, the philosophy that has been described by Bondi in the phrase "the universe is what it is, because it was what it was."

If we give up first causes, how then are we to understand the special significance of the time system implied through-out the above discussion? Write $t = C$. Here the C-field is a physical quantity. At each point of space-time the C-field has a definite numerical value that is quite independent of how we choose our coordinates. In writing $t = C$ we are making an explicit choice for the time coordinate, and we are defining what we mean by simultaneity. The time is the same at all points for which C has the same value. The definition of simultaneity is now physical, not geometrical. In the steady-state theory described above the relation $t = C$ is indeed satisfied.

A final question: Why should the distribution of matter in the universe be more simply described in terms of this choice for the time coordinate? At an earlier stage I spoke of energy and momentum of created particle(s) being equal to that carried by the C-field. The latter has a direction perpendicular to the surfaces of constant C. Hence particle(s) are created wtih their energy-momentum vector perpendicular to a surface of constant C, which, by our definition of t, is also a surface of constant time. It is this property that introduces the simplicity of description.

5

A Radical Departure
from the Steady-State Concept

A great deal of the argument of the previous chapter depended on the following restrictions:

(i) There should be no privileged position in the universe, no center, no place where things look any different from any other place.

(ii) From your own position things look the same in all directions.

These restrictions were considered to hold *in the large*, that is to say on a scale much larger than the galaxies, which were thought of simply as "particles" in a lattice. It was the properties of the large-scale lattice with which we were concerned.

Obviously, these restrictions do not apply on a small scale. A glance in the direction of the sun shows that things are locally quite different in that direction from what they are over the rest of the sky. Two problems immediately arise:

(1) How are we to reconcile large-scale homogeneity and isotropy with small-scale nonhomogeneity and nonisotropy?

(2) What determines "scale" in this sense—in particular, what is "large scale?"

In these questions we have further deep-rooted aspects of cosmology, to which there are as yet only tentative answers. Even an attempt to answer the second question on an empirical basis, by a direct appeal to observation, has reached no very clear conclusion. Certainly, "large scale" means much larger than the dimension of a galaxy. Opinion would favor a scale of about 100 million light-years, which is about 1 per cent of the greatest distances accessible to observation. Only on a scale larger than this can we employ the concepts of homogeneity and isotropy. In terms of *volume,* the localities in which nonhomogeneity and nonisotropy must be considered to exist comprise about one part in a million of the whole volume of the observed universe.

The orthodox cosmologies, described in the first part of the previous chapter, do not lead to a satisfactory answer to the first of the above questions. The Einstein–de Sitter cosmology, referred to as the $+\frac{1}{2}$ cosmology, has an advantage over the other cases, however. Small initial inhomogeneities become more marked as time goes on, so it is argued that the observed inhomogeneities, the galaxies and clusters of galaxies, represent initial deviations from homogeneity and isotropy. But once again we are back at first causes—the universe is what it is because it was what it was.

The cosmology involving the C-field can no longer be strictly described as a steady-state cosmology as soon as we drop restrictions (i) and (ii). The mathematical equations of the theory continue to hold, *without any change whatso-ever*, when we pass to inhomogeneity and to a lack of iso-tropy. The equations are now more complicated to handle, however, and it is sensible to learn their properties by con-sidering relatively simple cases, rather than by seeking to solve them for the most general kind of problem. It is indeed natural to consider the case of a spherically symmetrical ob-ject immersed in an otherwise homogeneous and isotropic universe. If the object were removed we would of course be back with the situation considered in the previous chapter. Now we ask how the presence of the object changes the solution of our equations.

First, let us consider the stability of the object in the ab-sence of the C-field. Gravitation tends to promote an inward collapse, which will occur unless the gravitational force is balanced in some way. Inside a star the gravitational force is balanced by forces due to presssure. Inside a body of larger mass than a star, say 10^6 times the mass of the sun, the gravi-tational force can still be balanced by pressure, provided the body is sufficiently dispersed, i.e., provided it has a suffi-ciently large radius. As the radius is decreased a stage is reached at which the body becomes unstable against collapse, however. This critical radius is about three hundred times the "gravitational radius" of the object, which I had better explain in a little detail.

In the Newtonian theory, a particle initially at rest, which falls freely from a large distance to the surface of an object of mass M and radius R, arrives at the object with the speed $\left(\dfrac{2GM}{R}\right)^{\frac{1}{2}}$. If you insert the mass of the earth, about 6.10^{27} gm, and the radius of the earth, about 6.10^8 cm, in this for-mula, together with the numerical value of the constant G, the gravitational constant, you will obtain an answer of about 11 km per sec. This is the well-known speed of escape from the earth, so important in the moon project, for by reversing the problem it is also the speed with which a particle must be projected from the earth in order that it should move *out* to a large distance. Now it is always better to write one's equations in "dimensionless form." Instead of writing $V = (2GM/R)^{\frac{1}{2}}$, in which V is the velocity of escape, we can obviously write

$$\frac{V}{c} = \frac{1}{c} \cdot \left(\frac{2GM}{R}\right)^{\frac{1}{2}} = \left(\frac{2GM}{c^2R}\right)^{\frac{1}{2}},$$

where c represents the velocity of light. The quantity V/c, being the ratio of two velocities, is now a simple number. For the case of the earth it is a small number, about 3×10^{-5}; for the sun it is about 2.10^{-3}. Evidently, for any given mass M the ratio V/c increases as R is diminished, and for sufficiently small R the ratio increases to unity, i.e., for

$$R = \frac{2GM}{c^2}$$

This is the gravitational radius corresponding to the mass M. For the earth, the gravitational radius is about 1 cm, for the sun it is about 3 km, for an object of mass 10^6 times the sun it is some 3.10^{11} cm—about four times the actual radius of the sun.

The formula for V/c gives a value greater than unity for R less than the gravitational radius, but the formula is now quite invalid, because the Newtonian theory on which it is based is then no longer applicable, even as an approximation. Calculations must proceed in accordance with Einstein's General Theory of Relativity. Indeed, the quantity $2GM/c^2R$ is a number whose value decides the kind of problem we are dealing with. If this number is much smaller than unity the gravitational field is weak, Newton's theory gives a good approximation to the situation and the local geometry is little different from the geometry of Euclid. But as $2GM/c^2R$ rises toward unity the gravitational field becomes strong, and neither Newton's theory nor the geometry of Euclid is remotely applicable to the situation.

Returning now to the instability of our massive object, I said that instability occurred when the radius was about three hundred times the gravitational radius, so that $2GM/c^2R$ is $\frac{1}{300}$ and the field is tolerably weak. As collapse proceeds, $2GM/c^2R$ increases and we pass over to the strong-field case. This is the phenomenon of "gravitational collapse." But before we proceed to consider the strong-field case, the possibility of a catastrophic release of nuclear energy inside the body must be considered. Sudden collapse will lift the internal temperature sharply, and nuclear processes can increase enormously in rapidity. The situation turns out that if the mass is not too large the catastrophic release of nuclear energy can halt the inward collapse and can blow the object back outward, but not even nuclear processes are powerful enough to do this when the mass exceeds some 10^6 times the sun—the case we are now considering. What happens to the implosion of such an object? What is the final outcome of the collapse? The object retreats *inside* its gravitational radius and collapses into a singularity, and it does so in a quite finite length of time as measured by an observer who moves with the body. The singularity has the same mathematical properties as the singularities that appear in the orthodox cosmologies discussed at the beginning of the previous chapter.

We are now faced by a worrying situation. So far as cosmology is concerned, it is always possible to feel that the origin of the universe is a remote question belonging to the distant past, and that perhaps we should occupy ourselves with more immediate problems. Now, however, we have the following situation. Remove the pressure support inside the earth. In only about 5 minutes, *on your watch,* you will arrive at a singularity. Of course, it is not physically possible to remove the pressure support in the case of the earth. But this does not change the logic of the situation, because for massive objects *there is no pressure support*—they actually satisfy our assumed state of affairs for the earth. If such massive objects did not exist in nature we would only be concerned with the logical problem, but realization that objects, with masses perhaps up to 10^8 times that of the sun, exist in the strong radio galaxies and in quasi-stellar sources makes the problem a practical one.

Narlikar and I have found that the problem is drastically changed when the C-field is included in the equations. Objects bounce instead of imploding into singularities. That is to say, they take up an oscillating state. The quantity M used in defining the gravitational radius is a measure of the total energy within the object. Usually, the main contribution to the energy comes from the mass of the material—the usual $E = mc^2$ cliché. Now, however, we have to add the energy contribution of the C-field, and this comes in with a negative sign, so that M is reduced. The gravitational radius is correspondingly reduced. Although R becomes small before the bounce takes place, the object does not retreat inside its true gravitational radius, as is the case in the usual theory. It is this feature of the negative sign of the C-field contribution that makes the difference in the problem.

There is also a completely static solution for an object, with the usual gravitational force balanced by the effect of the C-field. In fact, the static solution is just a special example of the oscillating case. Imagine an object to oscillate between a minimum radius R_1 and a maximum R_2, and now progressively decrease the difference between R_1 and R_2 until they coincide. The gravitational parameter $2GM/c^2R$ can come very close to unity in the static solution, which means we have a strong gravitational field. Similarly, in the oscillating case, $2GM/c^2R_1$ comes close to unity. What is the effect of this on the creation of matter in the vicinity of an object?

The C-field incident on an object behaves in the same way as a light wave—it picks up energy as it falls through the gravitational field of the object. We can consider two analogous problems:

(a) A light quantum is incident from large distance on an object of mass M and radius R. When near the object, the quantum induces the creation of an electron–positron pair.

(b) The C-field is incident from large distance on the same object. When near the object, it induces the creation of at least one baryon and, perhaps, accompanying electrons or neutrinos.

In (a) the energy of the created electron–positron pair is equal to the initial quantum energy multiplied by the factor $(1 - 2GM/c^2R)^{-\frac{1}{2}}$ and this can be a large number—since $2GM/Rc^2$ is close to unity.

In (b) the energy of the baryon (and its accompanying particles) is increased by exactly the same factor above the energy of creation at large distance from the object. Whereas we expect particles created at large distance to be moving slowly, particles created in a strong gravitational field must move close to the speed of light, in order that they possess the necessary energy. They must be cosmic rays. Because we now realize that cosmic rays are associated with strong gravitational fields, massive objects, and perhaps with highly collapsed supernovae, it is natural to suppose that cosmic rays and the matter created in such fields are one and the same thing. Emergence of cosmic rays would be more likely in the oscillatory case than in the static case.

To obtain higher and higher energies $2GM/Rc^2$ must come closer and closer to unity. This means that the volume available for creation gets less, the higher the energy. The situation is shown schematically in Figure 17. Portions of three spheres 1, 2 and 3, . . . concentric with the body are shown. On sphere 1 the energy factor $(1 - 2GM/c^2R)^{-\frac{1}{2}}$ is twice what it is on sphere 2, and on sphere 2 it is twice what it is on sphere 3 . . . A calculation based on available volume (and also taking into account the effect of the gravitational field on time availability) leads to the expectation that the number

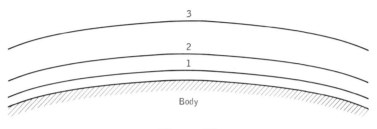

Figure 17

of cosmic-ray particles created in any range of energy, say the range from E to 2E, will be proportional to the inverse cube of E, E^{-3}. This agrees so well with the observed energy distribution of cosmic rays in the vicinity of the earth, and also with the energy distribution which cosmic-ray electrons must have in nearly all the strong radio sources, that evidently these ideas must be taken seriously.

A big difficulty appears, however, as soon as we attempt to match the predicted rate of creation of particles near a massive object to the observed rates of energy output from radio sources. The predicted rate is very much too small, so long as we stick to the value of the coupling constant f as determined in the fashion described in the previous chapter. It will be recalled that f is not determined by any theoretical consideration, but from an empirical fit to the observed rate of expansion of the universe. Suppose now we alter f to agree, not with the expansion of the universe, but with the creation requirement of the cosmic-ray sources. What kind of a cosmology emerges? A steady-state solution still exists, but it corresponds to nothing at all like the observed universe. The average density of matter, being just f in appropriate units, is greatly changed from the old value of 10^{-29} gm cm^{-3} to the far higher value of about 10^{-8} gm cm^{-3}. The radius of the observable universe is reduced from 10^{28} cm to 10^{18} cm, and the mass of the observable universe is reduced from about 10^{23} times the sun to about 10^{13} times the sun. Plainly, we are not living in such a steady-state situation. However, it is immediately interesting that the mass of the observable universe is now of the order of that of a typical group of galaxies. In the past no convincing explanation for this mass has ever been given. As we have seen, orthodox cosmologies are obliged to introduce "initial perturbations" in order to explain the galaxies and such perturbations are *adjusted* to give the right answer—an unconvincing procedure. In the old steady-state theory, attempts to explain the formation of groups of galaxies as condensations within a dispersed medium, density 10^{-29} gm cm^{-3}, did not turn out well either. Now that we see the typical mass of moderate clusters of galaxies appearing in a critical, fundamental way in the theory, it seems well worth pushing the situation further.

Before arriving at these considerations, Narlikar and I had already become worried about the local stability of the steady-state solution—this in the old theory. The steady-state solution is certainly stable to time-like perturbations so long as we stick to the restrictions (i) and (ii), the restrictions of homogeneity and isotropy. What we did was to abandon these restrictions, to consider the effect of local condensations of matter—the galaxies and clusters of galaxies. It appeared that the average rate of creation of matter may be controlled by the masses and radii of local condensations,

and by their number—rather than by the smooth homogeneous situation throughout space. This can be the case if the
number of condensations is not too large. In the opposite case
of a large number, the creation within one condensation
merges into that associated with neighboring condensations,
and we then have effectively the homogeneous situation. It
is possible for a large scale steady-state condition to be maintained through the combined effect of a number of localities,
each locally giving a greater contribution than the corresponding volume would do in the strictly homogeneous case.
Indeed, there is *always* a steady-state solution corresponding
to *any* distribution of local inhomogeneities. The steady
state corresponding to different distributions of inhomogeneities differ in the sense that they correspond to different effective values of the coupling constant f.

Now local inhomogeneities may be expected to change
with time. Their masses may increase due to creation. Expansion of the universe tends to reduce their density, unless
inhomogeneities divide into fragments, and so on. So long
as changes occur sufficiently slowly, the steady-state situation
corresponding to the currently existing inhomogeneities is
always maintained. It is as if the value of f were to fluctuate
slowly. Sudden changes in a particular region of space can
produce wide fluctuations from the corresponding steady
state, however. In exceptional situations it seemed to us as if
creation could be almost completely cut off, as if f were to
fall to zero. If this happened in a locality, say with dimension
a million light-years, the effect would be a fluctuation that
would develop into a state very like the observed universe.

With creation cut off in such a region, expansion proceeds
nearly as in the Einstein–de Sitter cosmology, the $+\frac{1}{2}$ cosmology. A difference arises because the region of instability
is localized. There is a maximum degree of expansion that
can occur before the region in question is filled in from sur-

rounding regions. The net effect is to set the localized region into a series of oscillations, so that the scale factor S for the region follows an undulating curve, as in Figure 18, instead of the smooth curve which would have been followed if no instability had developed. The amplitude of the oscillations

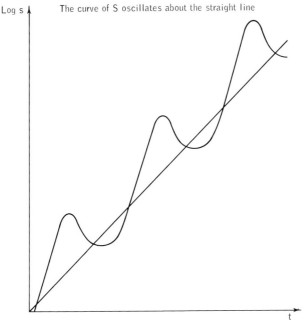

Figure 18

depends on the size of the region; the larger the region of instability the larger the oscillations.

Are we living in a fluctuation from a steady-state situation that operates at the high density of 10^{-8} gm cm^{-3}? Has the observed universe expanded from this density, and will it eventually fall back to it? Are we living in a kind of evacuated localized bubble? The balance of the evidence to all these questions is affirmative. Take first the problem of the condensation of galaxies. The Einstein–de Sitter relation between S and t possesses the important property that the material in any locality has the minimum energy necessary for unlimited expansion. A slight energy deficit in a particular locality will lead to the material expanding to a certain degree, a degree depending on the energy deficit, and then falling back to produce a local condensation. In our case, energy deficits occur in localities that possess inhomogeneities involving excess concentrations of material. Wherever there is a condensed blob of material, the blob will tend to check the outward motion of the surrounding material, leading to a condensation with the blob at its center. Such inhomogeneities will have masses less, probably appreciably less, than the steady-state mass of the observable universe, which is now about 10^{13} times the mass of the sun, and will have a size less than the radius of the observable universe, now 10^{18} cm, one light-year.

The reason why condensations must be on a scale less than the radius of the observable universe is contained in Figure 16, which shows that this radius represents a natural communication range. Nothing that occurs from now on at a particular point can be affected by current events at a distance greater than the radius of the observable universe. A single condensation could not span this radius because opposite sides of the condensation would get out of communication with each other.

It is possible to work out the amount of material that will be restrained from continuing expansion by a central blob of specified mass. If we require that expansion cease when the dimension of the whole localized system is of a galactic scale, say 100,000 light-years, then a central blob of mass 10^9 times the sun will restrain a total quantity of 10^{12} times the sun, while 10^7 times the sun at the center will restrain about 3.10^{10}

times the sun in total. Next, suppose the material condenses into stars, how will the brightness of the resulting object look, when seen in projection against the sky. Calculation shows that, except near the center, the surface brightness will fall off as the inverse ⅗ power of the distance from the center, a result in accord with recent observations by Liller for a number of nearly spherical galaxies. Here we have a remarkable agreement with observation. Other features of galaxies having appreciable ellipticity also follow from theory, such as the remarkable constancy of ellipticity for the different brightness contours, the isophotes. We also see why the elliptical galaxies have massive blobs at their very centers. According to the theory, the blobs are concentrated into regions less than 10^{18} cm in dimensions. These are the blobs that manifest themselves as radio sources. They are highly concentrated because they are leftover residues from the high-density state of the universe, the general state about which the oscillations of Figure 18 take place.

Several other features of the theory also fit immediately into line with observation. In this theory we expect the relation between $\Delta\lambda/\lambda$ and D to be that of the $+\frac{1}{2}$ cosmology. We expect the galaxies to fall between the zero curve and the $+1$ curve of Figure 1, and this they appear to do. The radio source counts of Ryle and Clarke no longer present the serious difficulty they do in the homogeneous steady-state theory. And the radio sources as the leftover residues no longer present any puzzle.

My impression is that the picture, briefly indicated above, of the formation of galaxies given by this theory may be decisive. If the theory is correct, it should be possible to make a real breakthrough into this hitherto intractable problem. What was said above refers to elliptical galaxies only. There is nothing to prevent material from condensing at much later stages of expansion, for example at the present epoch, if suitable pressure fluctuations exist in the intergalactic medium. In Chapter 3 it was pointed out that the pressure of cosmic rays could be important in this respect. Subsequent condensation has a critically different property from that described above. Above, we had material initially at high density passing to lower density through expansion, and of then being restrained from further expansion. The evolution is from high density to much lower density. Subsequent condensation, on the other hand, goes the opposite way—from low density to higher density. It is tempting to identify the second case with the formation of spiral galaxies, and with flat disks forming around elliptical systems. At the outset, in Chapter 1, we saw that there is considerable evidence to show that two methods of formation have been at work in the galaxies. In particular it appeared that our own Galaxy may be a two-component system. It seems that we are coming near to understanding the basis of the two components. Elliptical galaxies are simple expansion systems with relics of a former high-density state at their centers. Spiral galaxies are condensation systems probably involving high-energy particles and magnetic fields in their formation.

I would like to refer back to the effect of the C-field in preventing imploding objects from collapsing into singularities. An object of mass, say 10^7 times the sun, undergoes the bounce in quite a short time; with time measured by an observer sitting on the object, only about a hundred seconds. However, the time required for the bounce, as seen by a distant observer, can be something very different. The time is longer by the factor we used above $(1 - 2GM/c^2R)^{-\frac{1}{2}}$, in which the values of M and R at the bounce point must be used. Because $2GM/c^2R$ comes very close to unity, this is a large factor, and to the external observer the bounce seems to take a comparatively long time.

It is possible that we have here the explanation both

of the radio sources at the centers of galaxies, and of the quasars. Objects that began their implosion in the high-density phase, or even before that, *and which to observers attached to them have only gone through time intervals of a few minutes,* are now bursting out. To us on the outside there has been the long delay occasioned by the above factor. We may well be seeing objects that were typical of an entirely different state of our portion of the universe, of the steady state from which we have departed.

One might seek a similar explanation of the radio sources in the oscillating $+1$ cosmology. However, it must be remembered that, so far, no adequate explanation of the bounce of a massive object has been given in this cosmology.

To end this chapter—how big is the bubble in which we live? In expanding from a density of 10^{-8} gm cm^{-3} to 10^{-29} gm cm^{-3} the scale factor S has increased by 10^7. Hence, if the dimension of our instability was initially only a million light-years it is now some 10^{13} light-years in diameter, about a thousand times the portion of the universe visible in our telescopes. The universe as a whole still retains its steady-state characteristics, and the abstract considerations of the previous chapter—such as that concerning the asymmetry of time—still continue to hold. There will be other bubbles beside our own, and they will be of different sizes. It is an interesting speculation that some of the properties we observe in the laboratory, and which we tend to think of as invariable properties, may turn out to be fluctuation phenomena that depend on the size of our particular bubble. The particular values we find for the dimensionless numbers of physics, or of some of these numbers, could conceivably belong to our locality. If their values were different in other localities the full range of the properties of matter would be incomparably richer than it is usually supposed to be.

6

An Outline of the History of Matter

The history of matter is not the same as its origin. The history of matter is concerned with the building of the simplest building blocks, protons and electrons, into more complex atoms. Atoms consist of nuclei surrounded by electrons, and nuclei consist of a mixture of protons and neutrons. So, if we are to understand the building of nuclei, it will be necessary for some of the initial protons to switch into neutrons, which they can do by the β-process,

$$p + e^- \rightarrow n + \nu.$$

Here p represents the proton, e^- an ordinary electron with negative charge, n the neutron and ν a neutrino. Energy is needed to make this reaction "go," because the mass of the neutron is greater than the sum of the masses of the proton and electron, by roughly three-quarters of a million volts. The necessary energy comes, as we shall see, from heat inside stars.

In Figure 19 a few examples are shown of how the nuclei of familiar atoms are built from neutrons and protons. Over 1,400 different nuclei are known. Of these 280 are stable. Most of the unstable ones, some 1,100, are known only in the laboratory, because they decay quickly either by the β-proc-

NUCLEI

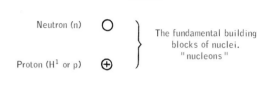

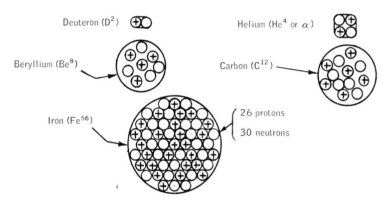

Nota bene:
All the nucleons are actually in rapid motion.

Figure 19

ess or by spitting out a helium nucleus consisting of two pro-tons and two neutrons. The β-process can take other forms besides that shown above, for instance

$$n \rightarrow p + e^- + \bar{\nu},$$

or

$$p \rightarrow n + e^+ + \nu,$$

where e$^+$ is an electron with positive charge, the antiparticle of e$^-$, and $\bar{\nu}$ is the antiparticle of the neutrino. A small fraction of the unstable nuclei decay very slowly, in times of the order of the age of the solar system. These are found on the earth, for example the isotopes U^{235} and U^{238} of uranium, the one with 92 protons and 143 neutrons, the other with 92 protons and 146 neutrons. The problem that faces us, in attempting to understand the history of matter, is to explain how all the nuclei found in nature, more than 300 of them, have been produced from protons and electrons. A detail is worth mentioning concerning the phrase "found in nature." With a single exception this means "found on the earth." The exception is the element technetium which is not found on the earth, except, of course, when it is made artificially in the laboratory. This one exception is observed in a certain class of stars, the S stars. Technetium lines appear in (d) of the third of the pairs of stellar spectra shown in Figure 20. This

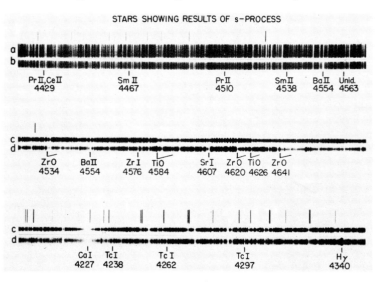

Figure 20

is the spectrum of the star R Andromedae. I will refer back to the first and second of these pairs of spectra at a later stage.

In the nineteenth century it was thought that all the different kinds of atom were immutable, that they were incapable of being changed one into another. To suggest otherwise immediately raised the charlatanic image of the alchemist. It seems to have been the English physicist William Prout who first noted that most atomic weights seemed to be multiples of that of hydrogen. He suggested that the heavier elements might be compounded out of the lightest one—hydrogen. But, as my friend William A. Fowler has pointed out, Prout did not see fit to sign either of his two articles on the subject, although he did sign his articles on the sap of the vine, the ink of the cuttlefish, and the excrement of the boa constrictor.

The physics of the twentieth century changed all this. The discovery of natural radioactivity showed that the elements are not immutable. The identification of isotopes (nuclei with the same number of protons but different numbers of neutrons) led to a revival of Prout's hypothesis. Those elements which did not have atomic weights approximately equal to an integral multiple of that of hydrogen—for example, the element chlorine—were shown to consist of mixtures of isotopes which did have this property. Then two converging lines of argument became decisive. By measuring the masses of atoms with much greater precision than before it was found that unprecedentedly great yields of energy might be obtained, either by fusing together two or more light elements or by breaking down the nucleus of a very heavy element. These results are summarized in Figure 21. The most strongly bound nuclei are those with atomic weights between about 50 and 65. Lighter nuclei are less strongly bound because of their larger surface to volume ratio and because a nucleon at the surface of a nucleus is less strongly bound than

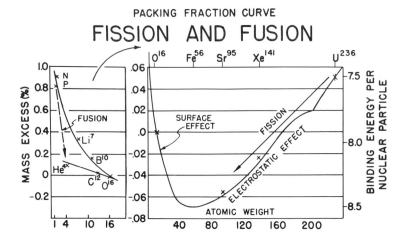

EINSTEIN'S RELATION: E = Mc²

E(Mev) = 931.15 M(AMU)

Figure 21

a nucleon in the interior. (By "nucleon" I simply mean a nuclear particle, a neutron *or* a proton.) Heavier nuclei, on the other hand, are less strongly bound because electrostatic repulsion effects increase with the nuclear charge. The balance between these two quite different physical effects lies in the region of atomic weights from 50 to 65. The element iron lies in the middle of this range, and the isotope Fe^{56} (26 protons, 30 neutrons) is one of the strongest bound of all nuclei. It turns out that it is just because of its strong binding that the element iron is so common in our everyday world.

This was the discovery of physicists, beginning with the work of Aston in the 1920's. Even earlier, it had become clear that in stars there must exist a vastly greater supply of energy than could ever be forthcoming from traditional sources; coal and oil, for example, were deficient by factors upward of a million. The natural inference, when the results of Figure 21 became known, was that processes of nuclear transmutation must be going on inside the stars. There were two possibilities, either light elements were being fused into heavier ones or very heavy elements were breaking down into lighter ones.

Jeans favored the breakdown of heavy elements, on the ground that fusion had not been shown to be experimentally possible, whereas breakdown was a known phenomenon for all elements heavier than bismuth. Eddington took the opposite view, arguing from his calculations that the internal temperatures of the stars were a critical factor in the problem, and this hardly seemed credible if the process were one of breakdown. To the physicists at that time, Eddington's argument seemed weak, because the temperatures he calculated, in the general region of 20 million degrees, appeared to be far too low to have a significant effect on fusion rates. This was before the development of quantum theory had revealed the important concept that the electric charge of a nucleus does not entirely protect the nucleus from collisions with other nuclei, even at the "low" temperatures that Eddington had calculated. The correct way to deal with such collisions was first worked out by George Gamow, and as a result of Gamow's theory it soon became clear that Eddington was not so wrong after all. In fact, Eddington has turned out to be entirely right. But this is in the sequel. In the 1920's, when things were not looking too bright, Eddington turned on his critics with the remark that if they didn't think fusion could occur inside stars then they had better go off and find a hotter place.

While the development of quantum theory changed the theoretical picture in a drastic way, the discovery that nuclei could be transmuted artificially by proton bombardment at moderate energies changed the experimental situation. It became possible for physics to answer the question posed by Eddington's calculations: What nuclear reactions can yield a significant supply of energy inside stars at temperatures no higher than about 20 million degrees? The answer was given in two parts, by Bethe and Critchfield, and by Bethe, following earlier work by Atkinson and Houtermans, and by Gamow and Teller. There were two possibilities that came to be called the proton chain and the carbon-nitrogen cycle. Details have changed in recent years, but the picture has not changed in principle. The details are shown in Figure 22 for the proton chain, and in Figure 23 for the carbon-nitrogen cycle. Both processes have the effect of converting hydrogen

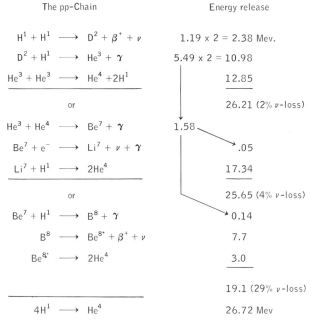

The pp-Chain

Energy release

$$H^1 + H^1 \longrightarrow D^2 + \beta^+ + \nu \qquad 1.19 \times 2 = 2.38 \text{ Mev.}$$

$$D^2 + H^1 \longrightarrow He^3 + \gamma \qquad 5.49 \times 2 = 10.98$$

$$He^3 + He^3 \longrightarrow He^4 + 2H^1 \qquad 12.85$$

or $\qquad$ 26.21 (2% ν-loss)

$$He^3 + He^4 \longrightarrow Be^7 + \gamma \qquad 1.58$$

$$Be^7 + e^- \longrightarrow Li^7 + \nu + \gamma \qquad .05$$

$$Li^7 + H^1 \longrightarrow 2He^4 \qquad 17.34$$

or $\qquad$ 25.65 (4% ν-loss)

$$Be^7 + H^1 \longrightarrow B^8 + \gamma \qquad 0.14$$

$$B^8 \longrightarrow Be^{8*} + \beta^+ + \nu \qquad 7.7$$

$$Be^{8*} \longrightarrow 2He^4 \qquad 3.0$$

19.1 (29% ν-loss)

$$4H^1 \longrightarrow He^4 \qquad 26.72 \text{ Mev}$$

Figure 22

The CNO-cycle   Energy release

$$C^{12} + H^1 \longrightarrow N^{13} + \gamma \qquad\qquad 1.95$$

$$N^{13} \longrightarrow C^{13} + \beta^+ + \nu \qquad\qquad 1.50$$

$$C^{13} + H^1 \longrightarrow N^{14} + \gamma \qquad\qquad 7.54$$

$$N^{14} + H^1 \longrightarrow O^{15} + \gamma \qquad\qquad 7.35$$

$$O^{15} \longrightarrow N^{15} + \beta^+ + \nu \qquad\qquad 1.73$$

$$N^{15} + H^1 \longrightarrow C^{12} + He^4 \qquad\qquad 4.96$$

or ($\sim 1/1000$)   (6% ν-loss) 25.03 Mev

$$N^{15} + H^1 \longrightarrow O^{16} + \gamma \qquad\qquad 12.11$$

$$O^{16} + H^1 \longrightarrow F^{17} + \gamma \qquad\qquad 0.59$$

$$F^{17} \longrightarrow O^{17} + \beta^+ + \nu \qquad\qquad 1.76$$

$$O^{17} + H^1 \longrightarrow N^{14} + He^4 \qquad\qquad 1.20$$

(10^{-3} x) 15.66 Mev

$$4H^1 \longrightarrow He^4 \qquad\qquad 26.72$$

Figure 23

into helium, exactly as Eddington had already guessed as early as 1920.

The energy yield from the conversion of hydrogen to helium is enormous. Conversion of only 10 per cent of the mass of the sun would give sufficient energy to keep the sun shining at its present rate for some 10 billion years, about twice the known age of the solar system.

Let us take a look at the stars in which these processes are going on. Plate XXXIII is the well-known cluster, the Pleiades, easily seen with the naked eye. The brighter stars of Plate XXXIII operate mainly on the carbon-nitrogen cycle. Plates XXXIV and XXXV show portions of the Milky Way. Most of the stars in these pictures operate on the proton chain. What decides which of the two processes is the more effective? Essentially the temperature does. At the lower temperatures, say 10 million degrees, the proton chain dominates;

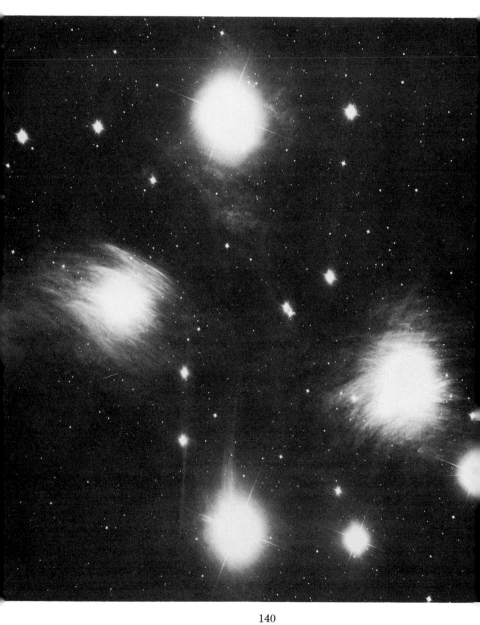

at the higher temperatures, above 20 million degrees, the carbon–nitrogen cycle takes over. Eddington's calculations already showed that the lower temperatures occur in faint stars of small mass, while the higher temperatures occur in bright stars of large mass.

Stars possess a very critical and important property, quite different from the ordinary objects of our everyday world. Take heat away from an ordinary object and it naturally cools down. Take energy away from a star and it somewhat unnaturally heats up! This difference arises because the gravitational field of the star produces a compression that raises the temperature. Suppose now that there was no conversion of hydrogen to helium inside a particular star because the temperature happened to be too low. The energy radiated into space away from the star's surface represents a removal of energy and, from what I have just said, the star would shrink. In doing so it would grow hotter. This would go on until the temperature became high enough for hydrogen to be converted into helium. In fact, the heating-up process would stop only when enough energy was produced from the nuclear reactions to compensate exactly for the loss rate. In this way we see that stars are self-stabilizing thermonuclear reactors, automatically adjusting their energy production to keep it equal to the leakage rate.

Stars with masses greater than the sun burn their hydrogen faster than the sun does, in some cases very much faster. This causes them to run into the problem of hydrogen exhaustion. What happens if the supply of hydrogen exhausts itself in the central regions of a star? From what we have seen the star, instead of cooling off, will shrink inward on itself and will

grow hotter as it does so. This raises the possibility that more complicated reactions than the simple conversion of hydrogen to helium may start up at the higher resulting temperature. Calculation shows that this indeed is the case, and that for a temperature of about 100 million degrees helium fuses to produce carbon, oxygen, and perhaps some neon. The details of how this happens are shown in Figure 24.

NUCLEAR PROCESSES IN STARS, I

Synthesis of helium and carbon

$$4H^1 \longrightarrow He^4 + Energy$$

$$He^4 + He^4 \rightleftharpoons Be^8$$

$$Be^8 + He^4 \longrightarrow C^{12} + Energy$$

Bethe's carbon-nitrogen catalytic cycle

$$C^{12} + H^1 \longrightarrow C^{13}$$

$$C^{13} + H^1 \longrightarrow N^{14}$$

$$N^{14} + H^1 \longrightarrow N^{15}$$

$$\underline{N^{15} + H^1 \longrightarrow C^{12} + He^4}$$

$$4H^1 \longrightarrow He^4 + Energy$$

Figure 24

A great deal depends on the experimental fact that two helium nuclei, two α-particles, do not form into a stable nucleus. Two α-particles coming together exist for a brief flash as the unstable Be^8, which breaks apart back to two alphas. Occasionally, during such a brief flash, a third α-particle comes along and adds itself to the other two with the emission of a quantum of radiation. The result is the common form of carbon, C^{12}. A further α-particle added to the

XXXIV (*opposite*). Constellation of *Orion* and surrounding region. Photographed with a Tessar lens of 10-inch focus. (Mount Wilson and Palomar Observatories.)

C^{12} produces the common form of oxygen, O^{16}. It is very likely this process of helium burning that produces the carbon and oxygen of our familiar world, the carbon in our bodies, and the oxygen we breathe.

Let us take a look at the kind of star in which helium burning goes on. In Figure 25 we have a form of the Hertzsprung-Russell diagram by Allan Sandage. The vertical coordinate represents luminosity, so that stars high in the diagram are bright, those low in the diagram are faint. Stars of high

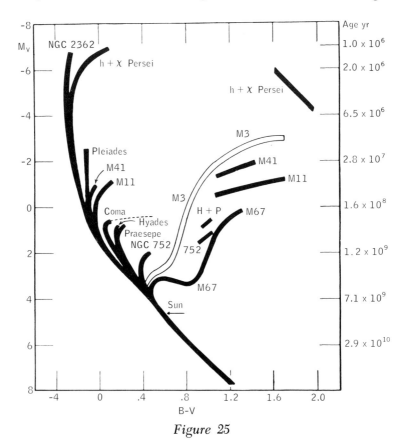

Figure 25

XXXV. Mosaic of the Milky Way, from *Sagittarius* to *Cassiopeia*.

surface temperature lie toward the left, those of low surface temperature to the right. In general, one can say that stars lying toward the upper-left corner are moderately large in size and are very bright, those toward the upper right—the giants—are both very large in size and very bright, while those low in the diagram are both small in size and faint, those low and on the left—the white dwarfs—are of very small size indeed, and are very faint.

In Figure 25, Sandage has indicated the places where individual stars are found in a number of star clusters—a cluster being a group of stars of essentially identical age—but with the stars differing from each other in mass, hence, in the speed of their internal nuclear reactions, and consequently in the rapidity of their evolution. The figure shows quite clearly that, as they evolve, stars move away from the main sequence, which slants from lower right to upper left, and they move into the territory of the giants. Moreover, calculation makes it clear that this evolutionary development is caused by the exhaustion of hydrogen in the central regions. It is among the giants that the fusion of helium into carbon and oxygen first arises. It is likely that in many giant stars *both* hydrogen burning and helium burning occur, but with helium burning near the center and hydrogen burning further out. This may be going on in many of the giants we see in the sky. Many of the stars in Plates XXXIV and XXXV are giants.

Before proceeding, I would like to indulge in one or two rather whimsical fantasies. Suppose that Be^8, the nucleus made up of two α -particles, had turned out to be moderately stable, say bound by a million volts. What would be the effect on astrophysics? Then helium would be a violently unstable nuclear fuel. The details of the way that helium burning begins in giants, the so-called helium flash, would be such that all giants would dissolve in violent explosions. There would be many more exploding stars, supernovae, than we actually observe. In Plate XX we had the well-known Crab Nebula, which may be the debris from a stellar explosion. We can be pretty sure that this explosion did not arise from the onset of helium burning, but from much more advanced stages of stellar evolution, the stages I shall be coming to in a moment. What I am saying now is that, if Be^8 were stable, the sort of thing we see in Plate XX would be very much more common. Indeed, it is possible that nothing more advanced in the way of stellar evolution could occur, that helium burning would terminate the whole nuclear development of a star. Certainly, carbon would be a far more commonplace element than it actually is.

Besides destroying the distribution of the chemical elements there would be other gross changes. For example, a large carbon excess would have existed in the material that went to form the planets of our solar system. Very likely a massive planet consisting largely of graphite would have condensed in the inner regions, in much the position we now find the planet Mercury.

The whole balance of the elements carbon and oxygen is critical not only for the chemistry of living organisms but for the distribution of the planets. If carbon were more abundant than oxygen it would be inevitable, I think, that a big graphite planet would lie nearest to the sun. And the balance of carbon and oxygen depends not only on the properties of Be^8, but on certain very fine details of the energy level schemes of C^{12} and O^{16}. We see these schemes in Figure 26 and 27. You notice that a level exists in C^{12} slightly above the sum of the rest-mass energies of Be^8 and the α-particle. This means that C^{12} can be formed in a resonant reaction, a property that speeds up the helium burning, tending to compensate for the instability of Be^8. In fact, by the combination of this resonance with the instability of Be^8 a sort of compromise situation is reached. Had Be^8 been stable, the helium-burning reaction would have been so violent that stellar evolution— with its consequent nucleosynthesis—would have been very limited in scope, less *interesting* in its effects. Had there not been a favorably placed resonance in the C^{12} nucleus, the rate of carbon production would be so slow that very little carbon would exist in the world; the opposite to the graphite planet situation. To refer lastly to O^{16}, if a similar favorably placed resonance existed in O^{16}, the conversion of C^{12} to O^{16} by α-particle addition would be so enhanced that once again there would be little carbon in the world. When we examine the O^{16} nucleus we see that a level exists very close to the sum of the rest masses of C^{12} and an α-particle, but fortunately the level is *below*, so that an actual resonance can never occur. I say fortunately, because if there was little carbon in the world compared to oxygen, it is likely that living creatures could never have developed.

The upshot of these remarks is that the further evolution

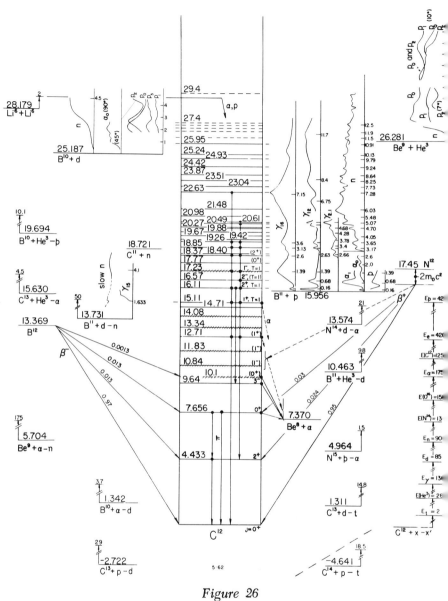

Figure 26

148

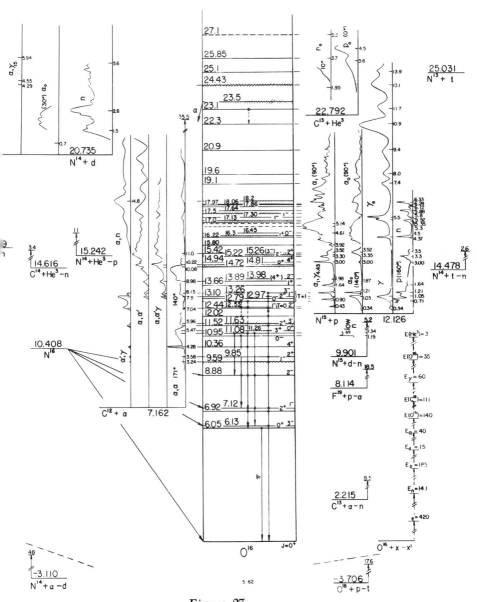

Figure 27

149

of stars leading to the synthesis of still more complex nuclei, combined with an approximately equal balance between carbon and oxygen depends on three apparently more or less random accidents—that Be^8 is unstable, that a resonant level exists in C^{12} at exactly the right place, and that a potentially dangerous resonance in O^{16} happens to be just below threshold.

I have referred several times to more advanced stages of evolution, but before I go on to discuss what form these more advanced stages take, it is worth noting that the explosions of stars such as we encounter in supernovae (Plate XX) has the effect of distributing stellar material in interstellar space. Such material can join the clouds of gas that exist in interstellar space, and can subsequently become recondensed into new stars. It follows that all except the first stars can contain material from previous stars. Therefore most stars at birth do not consist of precisely pure hydrogen. We evidently have the exchange scheme shown in Figure 28.

Next I want to apply the idea we had before, of hydrogen exhaustion leading to shrinkage and further heating, but now to helium exhaustion. Exactly the same thing can happen again. Following helium exhaustion, the temperature rises

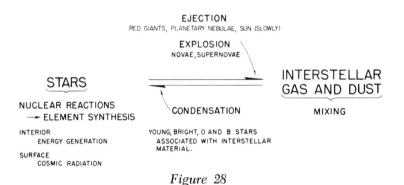

EJECTION
RED GIANTS, PLANETARY NEBULAE, SUN (SLOWLY)

EXPLOSION
NOVAE, SUPERNOVAE

STARS

INTERSTELLAR
GAS AND DUST

NUCLEAR REACTIONS
→ ELEMENT SYNTHESIS

CONDENSATION

MIXING

INTERIOR
    ENERGY GENERATION

YOUNG, BRIGHT, O AND B STARS
ASSOCIATED WITH INTERSTELLAR
MATERIAL.

SURFACE
    COSMIC RADIATION

Figure 28

and carbon and oxygen are themselves involved in further reactions. Their products are such elements as neon, sodium,
magnesium, aluminium, silicon, and sulfur. The same thing
repeated again leads to a burning of even these latter nuclei.
How far can we go with such a sequence of fuel exhaustion,
followed by shrinkage and heating, followed by the burning
of some new nuclear fuel? Not indefinitely, because there is
an end to the fusion reactions that yield energy. You will remember that the strongest bindings occur for nuclei with
weights from fifty to sixty-five. These nuclei do not burn to
yield energy. This range of atomic weights is the end of the
road, so far as nuclear fuel is concerned.

Therefore we expect that the net effect of stellar evolution
and of the burning of nuclear fuels is to fuse the initial light
elements, hydrogen and helium, to successively greater
atomic weights, until the range fifty to sixty-five is reached.
There we expect an increasing pile-up of material. This range,
which we often refer to as the "iron-group" elements constitutes the nuclear ash into which all lighter material is converted, granted the temperature rises high enough, to some
three billion degrees.

What predictions can we make? In Figure 29 we see a
schematic representation of the relative abundances of the
elements as they are believed to be in the solar system, and
in other stars like the sun. Notice the peak in just the range
of weights from about fifty to a little above sixty. Here is the
dead end we were speaking about. A peak occurs here exactly
because of the pile-up, because no further major fusion
processes can occur. This is where we find such elements as
chromium, manganese, iron, cobalt and nickel. The descend-
ing abundance from hydrogen to calcium we can easily interpret in the following way. Up to the present, only a fraction
of the hydrogen has been burned, this is why hydrogen is the
most abundant element. Similarly, only a fraction of the

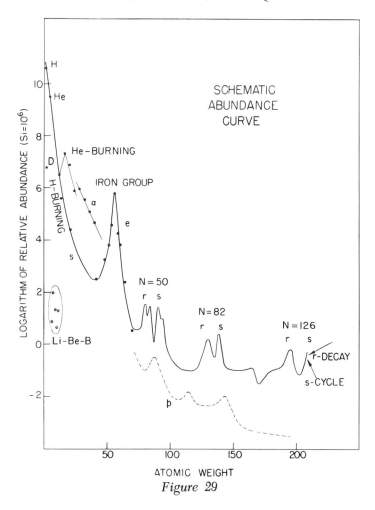

Figure 29

helium has been burned, and this is why helium is more abundant than carbon and oxygen. Similarly for the relation between carbon and oxygen on the one hand and magnesium and silicon on the other. The decreasing trend is only reversed for the iron group, and then because of the pile-up effect. The different letters you see in the diagram refer to various stages in the complex temperature evolution we have been speaking about. Before leaving this matter of the production of the iron-group elements, it is worth taking a detailed look at the calculated and observed abundances for

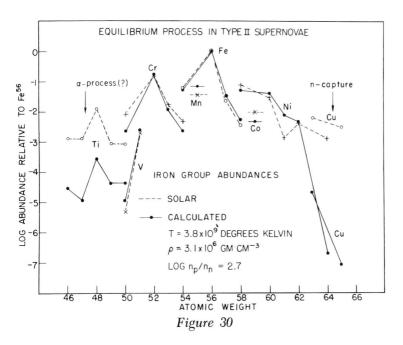

Figure 30

this group. The comparison takes the highly satisfactory form shown in Figure 30.

These ideas explain in a powerful way the evolution of matter from a starting point at hydrogen up to an atomic weight of about 60; that is to say, up to nuclei containing a total of about 60 nucleons, neutrons plus protons. But many nuclei are found in nature with atomic weights greater than this. Stable nuclei are found up to atomic weight 209, and the naturally radioactive nuclei are found up to the isotope of uranium with 92 protons and 146 neutrons. How were these formed?

Before offering an answer to this question, notice that we are only required to explain very small abundances of the heavy nuclei. The abundance scale in Figure 29 is logarithmic, from which you can see that typical abundances of the heavy elements are less than the hydrogen abundance by a factor 10^{10}. Hence quite a small by-product of our main process is sufficient to explain the synthesis of the very heavy nuclei. Indeed, the very low abundances of the latter make it clear that the processes leading to their synthesis *must* be in the nature of a by-product.

You may remember that the nucleus C^{13} is produced in the carbon-nitrogen cycle (Figure 24). After hydrogen exhaustion, when the temperature rises to that required for helium burning, somewhat above 100 million degrees, C^{13} combines with an α-particle to yield O^{16} plus a neutron. What happens to the neutron released in this way? Under suitable conditions the neutron adds itself, not to the more common light elements, but to the nuclei of the iron group. We have the

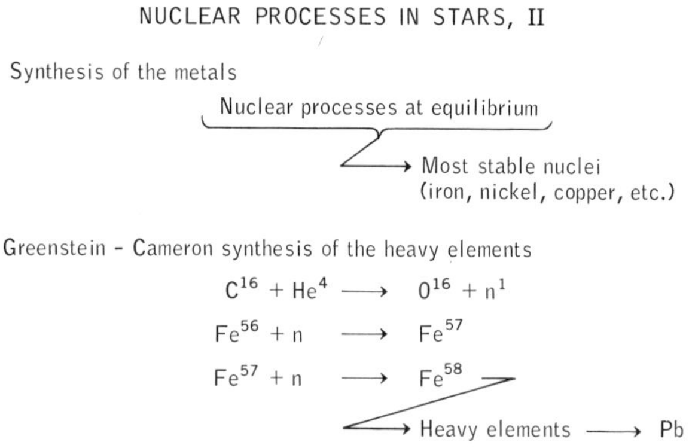

NUCLEAR PROCESSES IN STARS, II

Synthesis of the metals

Nuclear processes at equilibrium

⟶ Most stable nuclei
(iron, nickel, copper, etc.)

Greenstein – Cameron synthesis of the heavy elements

$$C^{16} + He^4 \longrightarrow O^{16} + n^1$$
$$Fe^{56} + n \longrightarrow Fe^{57}$$
$$Fe^{57} + n \longrightarrow Fe^{58}$$

⟶ Heavy elements ⟶ Pb

Figure 31

situation shown in Figure 31. And because there can be many more nuclei of C^{13} than there are of the iron-group we can have many neutrons for each iron-group nucleus, so that each such nucleus can pick up many neutrons, increasing its atomic weight substantially as it does so.

What proofs can we advance for this? First, we expect the product of the observed relative abundance and the neutron capture cross section (essentially the probability of a particular nucleus picking up a neutron) to vary smoothly from one atomic weight to the next. This is because a nucleus with a high capture probability will more readily be moved on to the next member in the series than will a nucleus with a low capture probability. In Figure 32 we see a plot of this product, given for approximately one-half of all the heavy nuclei. It is emphasized that measured cross sections and observed abundances were used in the construction of this figure. Particularly impressive are the two apparently discrepant cases. The discrepancies turned out to be due to wrong cross-section values, better values moved them down on to the curve, as you can see.

It is implicit in this curve that the nuclei with small cross sections, small probability of capturing neutrons, have comparatively high abundances. The outstanding cases are the elements strontium and barium. It is evidently of great interest that stars are known with spectra showing exceptional abundances of these elements. Indeed, the stars in question are known as Ba stars. Examples were already shown in Figure 20. There is a strong presumption that the elements strontium and barium were actually produced *in situ,* and hence that the process of neutron addition really does occur in stars. Stronger evidence for this, amounting to definitive proof, comes from the element technetium. Technetium has no stable isotopes and does not occur naturally on earth, but Te^{99} has a half-life of 2.10^5 years and is produced in the same

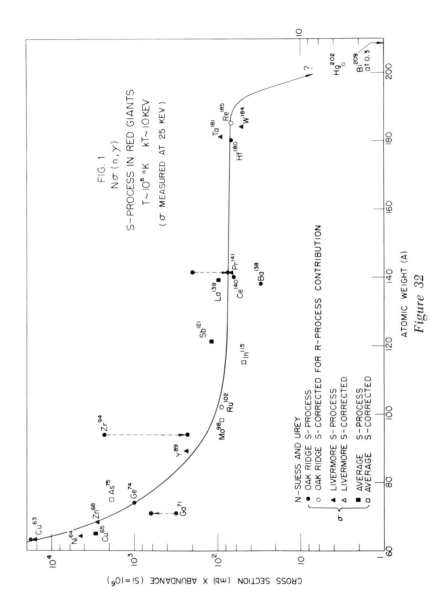

Figure 32

neutron-chain process as are strontium and barium. Technetium has been detected in a particular class of star, and an example of the spectrum of such a star is also shown in Figure 20.

Let us take a look at the details of the process of neutron addition, on the presumption that the neutrons are added rather slowly, say on a time scale of 10^5 years. This allows β-decay processes plenty of time to operate. A portion of the chain of neutron addition, passing through the elements cadmium, indium, and tin is shown in Figure 33. The important

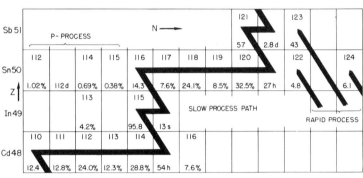

Figure 33

point emerges that not all of the observed stable isotopes of cadmium and tin are generated in this way. The track does not pass through Cd^{116}, or through either of Sn^{122} or Sn^{124}, because of the β-decays, which occur in time scales of the order of a day. To produce the missing nuclei it is necessary for a neutron chain to operate on a short time scale, say a few seconds so that these β-decays just do not have time to occur. Hence it is necessary that chains of neutron addition should occur slowly in some cases (for example during ordinary helium burning), and should occur very rapidly in other cases. We might, for example, associate the latter case with the conditions that occur in exploding stars, such as the case of the Crab Nebula (Plate XX).

I have put forward striking evidence in favor of the slow process. What evidence do we have for a rapid process of neutron addition? Well, it is possible to calculate the relative abundances of nuclei as we expect them to be produced in the rapid process. The results of calculation are shown in the

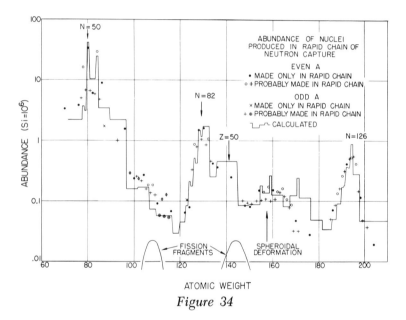

Figure 34

histogram of Figure 34, on which we also see the observed relative abundances of those heavy nuclei that were not displayed in Figure 32. The agreement between observation and the calculations is both striking and satisfactory.

In a single chapter, I am naturally able to give only a brief sketch of what is known concerning the relation of stars to the process of nucleosynthesis. I hope that in some degree I have demonstrated that we are not dealing in vague ideas, but that a good deal of quantitative calculation can be carried through, that we really do know something worthwhile about what goes on inside stars. Our knowledge is more complete in the nuclear aspects of the problem than it is on the astrophysical side, but this need not surprise us. In the last three decades vastly greater efforts have been made, and enormously more money spent, in understanding the fine details of nuclear physics than has been expended in astronomy. The workers in nuclear physics can be numbered in the thousands, against a few dozens in astrophysics. This situation has not been altered in any appreciable degree by the space program. While small fringe benefits to the study of the stars are coming, and will presumably continue to come, from the space program, it is as well to understand NASA exists in order to put a man on the moon. It so happens that I do not believe that anything really worthwhile will come out of the exploration of the slag heap that constitutes the surface of the moon, but my point now is not one of argument about whether the moon or the stars is the more interesting study. I am simply saying that the two are different and that nobody should imagine that the enormous financial budget of NASA implies that astronomy is now a well-supported subject. For a long time astronomy has been the poor relation of the physical sciences. The position is considerably better today than it was, but the poor relation still continues to be poor.

This would be a plaintive note to end with. Rather, I would like to refer back to my whimsical fantasies concerning the binding of Be^8, and the curious levels in the nuclei of C^{12} and O^{16}. I began what I regard as a fascinating topic of speculation, and then edged away from it. Obviously, at the present time we have more than enough to do in order to understand how the world works the way we find it. But I think one must have at least a modicum of curiosity about the strange dimensionless numbers that appear in physics, and on which, in the last analysis, the precise positioning of the levels in a nucleus such as C^{12} or O^{16} must depend. Are these numbers immutable, like the atoms of the nineteenth-century physicist? Could there be a consistent physics with different values for the numbers?

There seem to be two lines of attack on questions such as these, the first to demonstrate that the precise numerical values of the dimensionless numbers are all entirely necessary to the logical consistency of physics. The second point of view is that some, if not all, of the numbers in question are fluctuations; that in other places of the universe their values would be different. My inclination is to favor this second point of view, because certain numerical coincidences have the aspect of fluctuations (e.g., the ratio of electrical to gravitational forces is of the order of the square root of the number of particles contained within a cube of side c/H. H, the Hubble constant). On this second basis the curious placing of the levels in C^{12} and O^{16} need no longer have the appearance of astonishing accidents. It could simply be that since creatures like ourselves depend on a balance between carbon and oxygen, we can exist only in the portions of the universe where these levels happen to be correctly placed. In other places the level in O^{16} might be a little higher, so that the addition of α-particles to C^{12} was highly resonant. In such a place oxygen would be overwhelmingly more abundant than carbon, and creatures like ourselves could not exist.